NATIONAL OCEANOGRAPHIC DATA CENTER

GENERAL SERIES

QUESTIONS ABOUT THE OCEANS

PUBLICATION G-13

by
HAROLD W. DUBACH
and
ROBERT W. TABER

EDWIN J. SEREMETH
Technical Adviser For Graphics

Library of Congress Catalog Card Number: 67-60068

First Printing 1968
Second Printing 1968
Third Printing 1969

Published by the U.S. Naval Oceanographic Office
Washington D.C.   20390

*The National Oceanographic Data Center is
sponsored by U. S. Government agencies having an
interest in the marine environment; it is governed
by an Advisory Board composed of representatives of
these activities and the National Academy of Sciences.
The U. S. Naval Oceanographic Office is assigned
responsibility for management of the National
Oceanographic Data Center.*

The Sponsoring Agencies are:

Atomic Energy Commission

Bureau of Commercial Fisheries

Coast Guard

Coastal Engineering Research Center

Department of the Navy

Environmental Science Services Administration

Federal Water Pollution Control Administration

Geological Survey

Health, Education & Welfare

National Science Foundation

ACKNOWLEDGMENTS

The authors acknowledge with thanks the historical brief on the famous Woods Hole Oceanographic Institution vessel *ATLANTIS* supplied by Mr. Jan Hahn. The authors wish to give special recognition to the science class of Zundelowitz Jr. High School, Wichita Falls, Texas, which was a principal catalyst responsible for the creation of this book. We gratefully acknowledge the assistance of Mrs. L. Annette Farrall, Mrs. Wilhelmenia Bowe, and Mr. William Lyons.

PUBLICATIONS IN THE NODC GENERAL SERIES:

iv

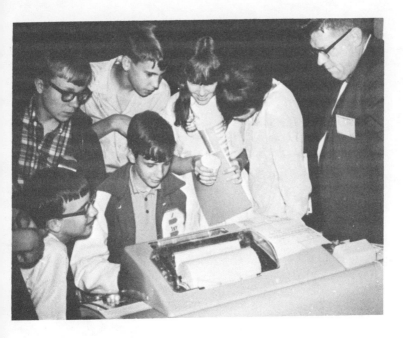

Junior High School Students Ask Questions About the Oceans at the
17th International Science Fair in Dallas, Texas.

THE OCEAN

Boats
float in it.
Fish
swim in it.
Stones
sink in it.
They all get wet.

CONTENTS

No.	Question	Page

No.	Question	Page

INTRODUCTION

In May 1966 the National Oceanographic Data Center was invited to be an exhibitor at the 17th International Science Fair in Dallas, Texas. Among other things, the display included a Teletype that linked the Fair exhibit to the NODC data-information base in Washington, D. C. Visiting teachers and students were invited to ask questions about oceanography and related subjects on the Teletype—and the Teletype quickly spelled out a response to the query. In some cases, answers were delayed because information was not in the data base; the question had to be referred to an experienced marine scientist. This exhibit became the "Fair favorite" as a constant stream of visitors waited their turn to ask a question and a crowd of curious onlookers waited for the answer to come in. The interest, curiosity, and enthusiasm shown by hundreds of Science Fair visitors from the southwest United States sparked the idea for this book. Their questions were limitless and their thirst for information on the ocean seemed never to be satisfied. At the conclusion of the Fair, the authors decided that a "question and answer" book on the oceans might be helpful and useful to many.

The questions presented in this booklet are typical of those asked by the Science Fair visitors or of the hundreds of student inquiries received each year by the NODC. And, of course, some questions are based on the authors' own personal contacts with individuals in all walks of life who wanted a specific question on the ocean answered.

One purpose of the book is to supply answers to the more commonly asked questions on oceanography and the marine sciences—but it is our hope that this book will fulfill a more basic twofold purpose:

(1) To present factual material on the marine sciences for use by young people at all grade levels, with the expectation that it will stimulate their imagination, create interest in the subject, and provoke further study; and

(2) To supply for teachers a suitable introduction to selected marine subjects, with specific references for additional information. (Additional assistance and study material are available from the National Oceanographic Data Center upon request.)

Each question and answer is followed by references containing more information on the topic. Answers may not cover some of the subtle details and related complexities, because the authors have made a concerted effort to supply an answer in 350 words or less. Particular attention was given to presenting the material in language understandable to the secondary school student. Elementary school children should be able to comprehend about 25 percent of the questions and answers.

The remainder probably will require explanatory help from the teacher or parents. Authoritative references containing additional details on each question are given; many of these books may be found in school libraries or can be easily obtained by instructors or students.

To our readers, we hope the information herein will promote further exploration into the wealth of material available on the oceans. We sincerely hope it will serve as a threshold to students seeking interesting challenges for study. To those who seek careers in virgin frontiers, we suggest serious consideration of the opportunities for investigation, research, and discovery in the marine sciences. If additional assistance or information is desired, we invite you to write us at the National Oceanographic Data Center.

1. What is the greatest depth of the ocean and where is it?

In 1959, the Soviet vessel VITYAZ reported a depth of 36,200 feet near the Challenger Deep. The Marianas Trench had been sounded in 1927 by the Japanese survey ship MANSHU, which recorded a depth of 32,190 feet.

In recent years, many other deeps have been measured by oceanographers; some of those reported by British and U. S. ships follow:

In 1952, the British survey ship CHALLENGER located a depth of 35,640 feet in the Marianas Trench off Guam (the Challenger Deep). This depth was measured by an echo sounder; it took 7-1/4 seconds for the sound to reach the bottom. To confirm the sounding, a weighted cable was lowered to the bottom; this lowering required 90 minutes.

On January 23, 1960, the bathyscaph TRIESTE descended into the Marianas Trench to a depth of 35,800 feet.

Although most publicity has been given to the Marianas and Mindanao Trenches, very deep soundings have also been recorded in the Southern Hemisphere. In 1952, the U. S. research vessel HORIZON recorded a depth of 34,884 feet in the Tonga Trench, south of Samoa Islands.

Gaskell, T. F.
   World Beneath the Oceans, American Museum of Natural History, 1964.
Soule, Gardner
   The Ocean Adventure, Appleton-Century, 1966.
Stewart, Harris B., Jr.
   Deep Challenge, Van Nostrand, 1966.

2. Why is the ocean blue?

Not all sea water is blue. Water of the Gulf Stream, off the eastern coast of the United States, is a deep blue, but water of a similar current off Japan is so dark that it has been named Kuroshio (Black Stream). In other areas water may be various shades of green, brown, or brownish-red.

The sea is blue for the same reason that the sky is blue. The blue of the sea is caused by scattering of sunlight by tiny particles suspended in the water. Blue light, being of short wave length, is scattered more effectively than light of longer wave lengths.

Although waters of the open ocean are commonly some shade of blue, especially in tropical or subtropical regions, green water is commonly seen near coasts. This is caused by yellow pigments being mixed with blue water. Microscopic floating plants (phytoplankton) are one source of the yellow pigment. Other microscopic plants may color the water brown or brownish-red. Near shore silt or sediment in suspension can give waters a brownish hue; outflow of large rivers can often be observed many miles offshore by the coloration of suspended soil particles.

The color of the sea changes constantly because of clouds passing across the face of the sun or because of the angle of the sun's rays passing through the atmosphere.

Oceanographers record the color of the ocean by comparison with a series of bottles of colored water known as the Forel scale.

Bowditch, Nathaniel
   American Practical Navigator, U. S. Naval Oceanographic Office, 1958.
Carrington, Richard
   A Biography of the Sea, Basic Books, 1960.
Miller, Robert C.
   The Sea, Random House, 1966.

3.   Where do waves come from?

The commonly seen waves on the surface are caused principally by wind. However, submarine earthquakes, volcanic eruptions, and tides also cause waves.

A breeze of less than 2 knots (2 nautical miles per hour) can form ripples. As the wind speed increases, larger more visible waves form. The wave height in feet usually will not be more than half the wind speed in miles per hour, although individual waves may be higher.

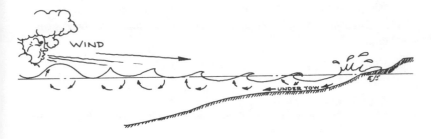

As long as the wind blows consistently from the same direction, the waves are referred to as sea. When the wind stops or changes direction, the waves that continue in a direction different from that of the local winds are called swell.

Bowditch, Nathaniel
   American Practical Navigator, U. S. Naval Oceanographic Office, 1958.
Gaskell, T. F.
   World Beneath the Oceans, American Museum of Natural History, 1964.
Miller, Robert C.
   The Sea, Random House, 1966.

4. What is the rate of sediment deposition on the sea floor?

Probably the most accurate method of dating sediments is the radio-carbon method. Red clay accumulates on the bottom of the deep ocean at a rate of half a centimeter or less every 1,000 years. Calcareous oozes may accumulate twice as fast.

The average deposition rate in the Atlantic is probably twice that in the Pacific, because much of the Pacific is far from the land which serves as a sediment source.

Very long cores (about 60 feet) brought up from the ocean floor contain sediments deposited over a time span of nearly 2 million years.

Deposits near land are so variable that no meaningful figures can be given.

Ericson, David B. and Goesta Wollin
   The Deep and the Past, Alfred A. Knopf, 1964.
King, Cuchlaine A. M.
   Oceanography for Geographers, Edward Arnold Ltd. (London), 1962.
Yasso, Warren E.
   Oceanography, A Study of Inner Space, Holt, Rinehart and Winston, 1965.

5. How thick is the ice in the Arctic Ocean?

The average thickness of the Arctic ice pack is about 9 to 10 feet, although in some areas it is as thick as 65 feet, with pressure ridges extending downward into the ocean as much as 125 feet.

The atomic submarine NAUTILUS passing beneath the North Pole on August 3, 1958, measured a pressure ridge extending 25 feet down. The depth of the ocean at the North Pole was recorded as 13,410 feet; depths as great as 13,776 feet have been recorded near the Pole.

Ice floes ranging from 7 to 13 feet in thickness have been reported in the Arctic. Icebergs, which are pieces of glacial ice floating in the sea, are many times thicker than sea floes.

Engel, Leonard and Editors of LIFE
    The Sea, Life Nature Library, Time, Inc., 1961.
Soule, Gardner
    The Ocean Adventure, Appleton-Century, 1966.

339-926 O - 69 - 2

6. If all the ice in the world should melt, what would happen?

The possibility that all the ice in the world would melt is extremely remote. If it should happen, the time span would be measured in thousands of years and the increased weight of the water would probably cause the ocean basins to sink and the land masses to rise.

In the unlikely event that all the world's ice would suddenly melt, the sea level all over the world could rise as much as 500 or 600 feet. The Antarctic ice cap alone covers 6 million square miles and, if melted, would yield about 6.5 million cubic miles of water, enough to feed the Mississippi for more than 50,000 years.

A rise of even 100 feet would flood most of the Atlantic seaboard of the United States, including all the major cities. A rise of 600 feet would cause the seas to cover 85 or 90 percent of the earth's surface (the oceans now cover about 71 percent of the earth's surface). The United States would be split in two by the "Mississippi Sea" which would join the Gulf of Mexico with the Great Lakes.

On the basis of evidence gathered from all over the world, Dr. Rhodes Fairbridge of Columbia University concludes that some 6,000 years ago the oceans rose about 14 meters within a few centuries, flooding almost all the areas where man had begun to found civilizations. He believes this to be the same Great Flood described in the Bible, in Buddhist records, and in legends handed down in many lands.

There is also the possibility that the ice age is not yet over and that the ice caps may again increase in size. If another glacial advance comparable to the last one should occur, many of the important manufacturing and agricultural areas of the world would be covered, forcing widespread migrations.

Ericson, David B., and Goesta Wollin
   The Deep and the Past, Alfred A. Knopf, 1964.
Freuchen, Peter
   Peter Freuchen's Book of the Seven Seas, Julian Messner, 1957.
Gaskell, T. F.
   World Beneath the Oceans, American Museum of Natural History, 1964.

7. What causes the red tide?

The red tide and its effects on fish have been known since Biblical times. Dr. Harris B. Stewart, Jr., Director of the Institute for Oceanography of the Environmental Science Services Administration, says that probably this particular phenomenon had occurred in the lower Nile and is recorded in the Bible in the seventh chapter of Exodus ". . . .and all the waters that were in the river were turned to blood, and the fish that were in the river died; and the river stank, and the Egyptians could not drink the waters of the river."

A red tide, with its mass fish kill, occurs when the following two conditions exist: (1) physical factors are favorable to the rapid reproduction of dinoflagellates *(Gymnodinium),* and (2) the number of predators is temporarily reduced. Dinoflagellates are one-celled organisms with characteristics of both plants and animals. Although less than a thousandth of an inch in size, they reproduce so rapidly that a quart of sea water may contain 100 million.

Millions of fish may be killed during such a plankton "bloom." More than 50 million were reported killed off Florida in 1947.

Deacon, G. E. R. (Ed.)
Seas, Maps, and Men, Doubleday and Company, 1962.
Stewart, Harris B., Jr.
Deep Challenge, Van Nostrand, 1966.
Troebst, Cord-Christian
Conquest of the Sea, Harper and Row, 1962.

8.   What makes the ocean salty?

For many years it was assumed that the ocean began as fresh water and that the age of the earth could be determined by comparing the annual increase of salt from rivers with the total salt in the ocean. However, radioactive dating of rocks indicates that the earth is much older than the age derived by such method.

It is now generally believed that the primeval seas were initially salty, having dissolved their salts from the rocks underlying their basins. Breaking up of continental rocks by frost and erosion has added to the salts of the sea, but the dissolved material in rivers contains higher percentages of carbonates than does sea water, where chlorides predominate.

The saltiness of the oceans is undoubtedly increasing, but it is a slow process which has been going on for hundreds of millions of years.

Carrington, Richard
   A Biography of the Sea, Basic Books, 1960.
Engel, Leonard, and Editors of LIFE
   The Sea, Life Nature Library, Time, Inc., 1961.
Miller, Robert C.
   The Sea, Random House, 1966.

9. Is there gold or other precious elements in the ocean? If so, how much?

Yes, there are traces of many valuable elements in the ocean, including gold and silver. The trouble is that these are present in very minute concentrations. For example, there is not enough gold in a cubic yard of sea water to cover the period at the end of this sentence, and it would be worth less than 0.1 of a cent. Its extraction would cost more than the value of the gold.

Although analyses of sea water samples from various parts of the ocean differ only slightly when a volume of one cubic yard of sea water is considered, extrapolations for the amount of gold in a cubic mile magnify substantially the analytical differences and geographic variations. Carson calculates 93 million dollars worth of gold in a cubic mile; Pincus sets the value at 20 thousand dollars.

After the First World War, Germany seriously considered extracting gold from the ocean to pay the war debt. The idea was endorsed and supported by the distinguished chemist Fritz Haber. One of the main goals of an extended series of expeditions by the METEOR, which crossed and recrossed the North and South Atlantic repeatedly between 1924 and 1928, was to investigate the feasibility of gold recovery from the ocean. Although the quantity of gold found was less than expected and the cost of extraction prohibitively high, the METEOR collected much valuable oceanographic data.

If a "cheap" industrial method of extracting gold from the sea is ever developed, gold would lose much of its value.

Carson, R. L.
   The Sea Around Us, Oxford University Press, 1951; Mentor Books (Paperback), 1954.
Clarke, Arthur C.
   The Challenge of the Sea, Holt, Rinehart and Winston, 1960.
Pincus, Howard J.
   Secrets of the Sea, Oceanography for Young Scientists, American Education Publications, Inc., 1966.

10. What is the difference between a sea and an ocean?

The terms "sea" and "ocean" are often used interchangeably in referring to salt water. However, from a geographic point of view, a sea is a body of water that is substantially smaller than an ocean or is part of an ocean.

The term "seven seas" dates back to ancient times, referring to the seas known to the Mohammedans before the 15th century. These were the Mediterranean Sea, the Red Sea, the East African Sea, the West African Sea, the China Sea, the Persian Gulf, and the Indian Ocean.

In more recent times, Rudyard Kipling popularized the expression "seven seas" by using it as the title of a volume of poems. There has been a tendency to divide the world's ocean into seven oceans to retain this legendary number. The popular division is Arctic, North Atlantic, South Atlantic, North Pacific, South Pacific, Indian, and Antarctic. However, International Hydrographic Bureau at Monaco does not accept the existence of an Antarctic Ocean. Actually, of course, all limits of oceans are arbitrary, as there is only one global sea. The International Hydrographic Bureau subdivisions are primarily for the purpose of filing *Notices to Mariners* and have little to do with natural boundaries.

The International Hydrographic Bureau lists 54 seas; some are seas within seas. The Mediterranean Sea contains seven seas so one could sail the seven seas (of the Mediterranean) without ever venturing into an ocean.

Freuchen, Peter
    Peter Freuchen's Book of the Seven Seas, Julian Messner, 1957.
International Hydrographic Bureau
    Limits of Oceans and Seas, Special Publication No. 23, Monaco, 1953.
Pell, Claiborne (Senator)
    Challenge of the Seven Seas, William Morrow and Company, 1966.

11. How deep has a skin diver gone?

The greatest depth to which a diver has ever descended without a pressure suit was reached in December 1962 when Hannes Keller, a Swiss mathematician, and Peter Small, a British journalist, descended to 1,000 feet in an open diving bell. At that depth, Keller swam outside

for 3 minutes. He breathed a secret mixture of gases which was based on his own computations of what the human system requires and can tolerate; he also computed the decompression stages for the diver. Unfortunately, Small and another diver died during this attempt.

The deepest dive without breathing aids, mask, or fins was made in February 1967 by Robert Croft, a U. S. Navy submarine escape instructor. He carried a 29-pound weight and reached a depth of 212.7 feet. His unusual ability can be attributed to the fact that he had rickets in his childhood, which resulted in a flexible rib cage and a lung capacity about twice the normal.

Dugan, James and Richard Vahan (Ed.)
   Men Under Water, Chilton Books, 1965.
Link Edwin A.
   "Tomorrow on the Deep Frontier," *National Geographic,* Vol. 125, No. 6, June, 1964.
Miller, Robert C.
   The Sea, Random House, 1966.

12. Can a "hard hat" diver go deeper than a skin diver?

Going to great depths presents many problems to a hard hat diver. First of all, he is tied to the surface by breathing tubes. Also, the high air pressure causes some of the nitrogen in the diver's air supply to dissolve in his blood (air is composed of about 80% nitrogen, 20% oxygen). The emergency limit for Navy divers is about 500 feet, although divers have gone much deeper.

The main advantages of the hard hat gear are that the diver has protective clothing and telephone connections to the surface. A helmet diver could spend perhaps 3 or 4 hours working at 200 feet, but he would then have to make a very slow return to the surface.

Scuba divers have more mobility, but in practice they are limited to less than 200 feet, unless they have a special diving apparatus and gas mixtures. A "closed circuit scuba," which has been tested at depths of 600 feet by Westinghouse Underseas Division, is expected to provide safe breathing mixtures at depths exceeding 1,000 feet. This would provide the capability of working at great depths for extended periods.

The underwater structures, tested by Cousteau and Link, from which scuba divers emerge to work, make it possible for divers to live and work under water for weeks at a time.

Gaskell, T. F.
  World Beneath the Oceans, American Museum of Natural History, 1964.
Pell, Claiborne (Senator)
  Challenge of the Seven Seas, William Morrow and Company, 1966.
Rebikoff, Dimitri
  Free Diving, E. P. Dutton and Company, 1956.

13. How deep has man gone in the ocean?

On January 23, 1960, Jacques Piccard and Lt. Donald Walsh, USN, descended in the bathyscaph *TRIESTE* to a depth of 35,800 feet at the bottom of the Challenger Deep (Marianas Trench), the deepest spot in the ocean known at that time (see question 1). At that depth, the temperature was 2.4°C (36.5°F).

During the descent they passed a minimum temperature of 1.4°C at 2,000 fathoms.

The *TRIESTE* was designed and constructed by Jacques' father, Auguste Piccard, the famous Swiss explorer of the stratosphere. It was launched in the Mediterranean in 1953 and acquired by the U.S. Navy in 1958.

The record descent of the *TRIESTE* took 4 hours and 48 minutes. The return to the surface required 3 hours and 17 minutes.

Gaskell, T. F.
   World Beneath the Oceans, American Museum of Natural History, 1964.
Piccard, Jacques, and Robert S. Dietz
   Seven Miles Down, G. P. Putnam's Sons, 1961.
Soule, Gardner
   The Ocean Adventure, Appleton-Century, 1966.

14. What is the source of the Gulf Stream?

The Gulf Stream received its name because of the misconception that its source was the Gulf of Mexico. It is now known that water of the Gulf contributes very little to the flow of the Gulf Stream.

Two currents, the North and the South Equatorial Currents, join to flow through the passages between the Windward Islands into the Caribbean Sea. The resultant current, flowing through the Yucatan

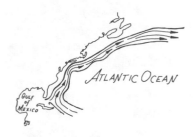

Channel, has only one outlet between Florida and Cuba. Off the southern coast of Florida, other currents coming from the northern coast of Puerto Rico and eastward from the Bahamas add to the flow of the Gulf Stream.

Bowditch, Nathaniel
   American Practical Navigator, U. S. Naval Oceanographic Office, 1958.
Stommel, Henry
   The Gulf Stream, University of California Press, 1958.
U. S. Naval Oceanographic Office
   Science and the Sea, Washington, D. C., 1967.

15. How long (and big) is the Gulf Stream?

It is difficult to set exact boundaries for the Gulf Stream. There is much meandering, with eddies and offshoots. Also, the Gulf Stream is part of a larger system, known as the Gulf Stream System, which encompasses the entire northward and eastward flow from the Straits of Florida, including the branches crossing the North Atlantic from the region south of the Newfoundland Banks. The Gulf Stream proper is the portion between the Straits of Florida and the Grand Banks.

The flow of water through the Straits of Florida is about 26 million cubic meters per second. By the time the Stream reaches Chesapeake Bay, the transport has increased to 75-90 million cubic meters per second because of the addition of Sargasso water and deep water. Beyond the Grand Banks, the flow decreases to less than 40 million cubic meters per second, since part of the water turns southward.

Carson, R. L.
> *The Sea Around Us,* Oxford University Press, 1951; Mentor Books (Paperback), 1954.

Stommel, Henry
> *The Gulf Stream,* University of California Press, 1958.

U. S. Naval Oceanographic Office
> *Science and the Sea,* Washington, D. C., 1967.

16. What is a waterspout and what causes it?

A waterspout is a funnel-shaped column or spout of water extending from the sea to a cloud and sustained by a circular wind movement.

Waterspouts result from meteorological causes. Atmospheric conditions associated with waterspouts are unstable. The air temperature may be much lower than the sea surface temperature. Thunder and lightning often accompany the phenomenon. They occur most frequently in the tropics, but are also known in temperate zones.

The occurrence and movement of waterspouts are unpredictable. They may occur in gales or calms, move with or against the winds, rotate either clockwise or counterclockwise, and move slowly or rapidly. Winds in the most severe spouts may exceed 200 miles per hour.

Heights from 10 to 5,000 feet and widths from 10 to 500 feet have been reported.

On June 25, 1964, meteorologists had an opportunity to observe waterspouts at close range at the Tampa airport. At the time meteorological conditions were very unstable, and severe thunderstorms had occurred just before the spouts were observed. The sustained measured wind speed was 67 miles per hour, with gusts of 79 miles per hour. During this period, 1-3/4 inches of rain was recorded in 40 minutes, accompanied by hail. The total distance covered by the spouts was about 10 miles; the average speed of advance of the waterspouts was 30 miles per hour.

Miller, Robert C.
  The Sea, Random House, 1966.
U. S. Naval Oceanographic Office
  Science and the Sea, Washington, D. C., 1967.

17. What do oysters and clams eat?

Oysters and clams eat microscopic plants called phytoplankton, which live in the water. Oysters and clams spend most of their time attached to or buried in the bottom and do not move around searching for food. They obtain food by pumping water through their bodies. Clams and oysters, like fish, breathe by means of gills, but their gills also act as a sieve, straining the phytoplankton out of the water. The gills are covered with a sticky substance which holds the phytoplankton. Tiny hairs, called cilia, move the food from the surface of the gills to the

mouth. Pieces of food too large for the animal to eat are discarded and flushed out of the body by the water current. A single blue mussel will pump about 10 gallons of water a day, filtering out the plankton and debris that make up its diet.

Of the various nutrients that have been experimentally tried as food supplements for oysters, finely ground corn meal was found to be acceptable and resulted in fatter oysters.

Barnes, Robert D.
  Invertebrate Zoology, W. B. Saunders Company, 1964.
Cromie, William J.
  The Living World of the Sea, Prentice-Hall, 1966.
Galstoff, P. S.
  "The American Oyster (Crassostrea virginica Gmelin)," U. S. Department of the Interior, Fisheries Bulletin 64: 1-480, 1964.

18. What commercial products other than fish are obtained from the sea?

Products obtained commercially from sea water include common salt, bromine, and magnesium. All of the United States' supply of magnesium is taken from sea water, because extraction is cheaper than obtaining it from mines on land. About 75 percent of our supply of bromine is extracted from the sea.

In recent years interest has developed in exploiting the seemingly inexhaustible supply of manganese and phosphate-rich nodules on the sea floor. The American Institute of Mining, Metallurgical, and Petroleum Engineers (AIME) has estimated that there are 1.5 trillion tons of manganese nodules on the bottom of the Pacific Ocean. These nodules contain as much as 50 percent manganese plus smaller amounts of nickel, copper, cobalt, and other metals. Nodules on the sea floor appear to be forming faster than the rate at which the United States is now using manganese, nickel, and cobalt; thus it seems that our reserve of these metals is assured for many years. Phosphorite nodules off the California coast could satisfy California's phosphate fertilizer needs for many years.

Other materials obtained from the sea floor or beaches include diamonds, pearls, sand, gravel, shell, and ores of tin, thorium, and titanium.

Oil is being recovered from beneath the ocean floor in increasing amounts. In 1960, about 8 percent of the free world's oil supply was obtained from this source; by 1965, it had increased to 16 percent. Undersea deposits of sulfur are also being tapped by drilling from platforms in the Gulf of Mexico, as the supply on land dwindles.

Carson, R. L.
   The Sea Around Us, Oxford University Press, 1951; Mentor Books,
   (Paperback), 1954.
Stewart, Harris B., Jr.
   Deep Challenge, Van Nostrand, 1966.
U. S. Bureau of Mines
   Mineral Yearbook, 1963, Washington, D. C., 1964.

19. What is the annual fish take by the United States?

According to the Bureau of Commercial Fisheries, commercial fishermen in the United States caught 4.3 billion pounds of fish in 1966. This was a decrease of nearly 10 percent from the 4.7 billion pound catch landed in 1965. However, the 1966 catch sold for 454.4 million dollars, nearly 21 percent over the average for the preceding 10 years. The 1963 catch of 4.6 billion pounds sold for only 390 million dollars.

Cromie, William J.
   The Living World of the Sea, Prentice-Hall, 1966.
U. S. Department of the Interior
   Fisheries of the United States, published annually.

20. How does the fish take of the United States compare with other countries?

In 1956, the United States ranked second in the world in fish catch; by 1966 the United States had dropped to sixth place. The catch by American vessels is less than one-twentieth of the world's total.

Today Peru leads the world in fish catch and landings, followed by Japan, Red China, the Soviet Union, and Norway.

The world's catch of seafoods of all types (chiefly fish) in 1966 is estimated at 123 billion pounds, an increase of 6 percent over 1965. Two-thirds of it went directly for human consumption.

Although the United States is not generally considered a fish-consuming country, the per capita consumption of fish in the United States is nearly double the world's average. Fish consumption in the United States is about 63 pounds (whole weight) per person per year.

The United States is the world's largest importer of fishery products. In 1966, about 65 percent of the U. S. consumption was imported.

Cromie, William J.
  The Living World of the Sea, Prentice-Hall, 1966.
Miller, Robert C.
  The Sea, Random House, 1966.
Pell, Claiborne (Senator)
  Challenge of the Seven Seas, William Morrow and Company, 1966.

21. What are the primary pollutants found in the sea and what are their sources?

Man is the greatest contributor of pollutants, such as sewage, pulp-mill wastes, fertilizers, soaps, detergents, radioactive wastes, synthetic fibers, plastics, oils, tars, greases, and insecticides. Hot and cold water discharged by factories and silt from dredging operations may also be considered as pollutant.

Radioactive wastes may be direct fallout, discharges from nuclear power plants, or nuclear waste disposed at sea.

Improperly treated municipal and industrial wastes, which have long presented problems in lakes, streams, and rivers, are becoming increasingly serious in nearshore oceanic waters.

Agricultural chemicals, both fertilizers and pesticides, are carried into the oceans by runoff and through the atmosphere.

Future coastal installations of large nuclear reactors that use sea water cooling could result in contaminants that would significantly affect the marine environment and the life it supports.

Gorsky, N.
  The Sea—Friend and Foe, Foreign Languages Publishing House, Moscow (Paperback), 1961.
National Academy of Science—National Research Council
  Oceanography 1966—Achievements and Opportunities, 1967.

339-926 O - 69 - 3

22. What is Atlantis?

The story of Atlantis is one of the most persistent of all legends. More than 5,000 scholarly works are in existence about the lost Atlantean civilization. The oldest existing account is that of Plato and is the basis for most subsequent speculations.

Plato described a great civilization far ahead of its time. The Atlanteans built temples, ships, and canals. They lived by agriculture and commerce. In their pursuit of trade, they reached all the countries around them. By 9600 B. C. they had conquered all the known world except Greece, which was saved when Atlantis was engulfed by the sea, overnight, disappearing without a trace.

Plato said that Atlantis was west of the Pillars of Hercules, which many people have assumed to be the Straits of Gibraltar. Recently it

has been suggested that the pillars may have been the Strait of Messina between Italy and Sicily.

Before entirely dismissing the legend as a myth, remember that for thousands of years the cities of Troy, Pompeii, and Herculaneum were considered to be mythical. It has been said that mythology is history seen through the eyes of the intellectually immature.

Clarke, Arthur C.
   The Challenge of the Sea, Holt, Rinehart and Winston, 1960.
Donnelly, Ignatius J.
   Atlantis: The Antediluvian World, Harper and Brothers, 1882.
Pell, Claiborne (Senator)
   Challenge of the Seven Seas, William Morrow and Company, 1966.

23. What does the sea floor look like?

The sea bottom is divided into three distinct areas: the continental shelf, the continental slope, and the ocean floor.

The continental shelf has numerous hills, ridges, terraces, and even canyons comparable to the Grand Canyon. The average width of the shelf is about 30 miles, but it may extend several hundred miles from shore. The continental slope, between the shelf and the deep ocean, has an average slope of 2 to 3 degrees, although the slope off a volcanic island may be as much as 50 degrees.

Features of the ocean bottom are comparable to those on land. Many mountains under the sea are higher than Mt. Everest. All oceans except the North Pacific are divided by an almost continuous system of mountains, the largest being the Mid-Atlantic Ridge.

Most of the deep-ocean floor is made up of basins surrounded by walls of lesser depth. Oceanographers have compared the floor of the Pacific to the surface of the moon.

Deep trenches rim the Pacific in areas associated with great volcanic activity and lie near islands and continental slopes. The deepest known trenches are in the Western Pacific.

Scientists once believed that the ocean floor was covered by a layer of recently deposited sediments, but it is now known that sediments deposited 100 million years ago lie near the surface of the ocean floor and in some areas are even exposed.

Engel, Leonard and Editors of LIFE
    The Sea, Life Nature Library, Time Inc., 1961.
King, Cuchlaine A. M.
    Oceanography for Geographers, Edward Arnold Ltd. (London), 1962.
Yasso, Warren E.
    Oceanography, A Study of Inner Space, Holt, Rinehart and Winston, 1965.

24. Are there strong currents at depths beneath the ocean surface that might compare to the "jet stream" in the upper levels of the atmosphere?

In 1952, Townsend Cromwell of the U. S. Fish and Wildlife Service began investigation of a previously unknown subsurface current flowing in a direction opposite to that of the surface currents. This current has speeds up to 3 knots and could be used by submarines to increase speed and reduce power requirements, just as the jet stream is used by high flying aircraft.

The Cromwell Current is a shallow current flowing eastward along the Equator beneath the South Equatorial Current. In certain places, it comes to within 100 feet of the surface; its bottom limit reaches a depth of 750 feet. The flow is equal to half the volume of the Gulf Stream and its extent is about 8,000 miles, from New Guinea to the coast of Ecuador.

A similar undercurrent is known to exist below the South Equatorial Current in the Atlantic. Investigations by British and American ships during the International Geophysical Year revealed that this current flows in a direction opposite to that of the Gulf Stream at speeds of 1.5 to 15 miles a day. This countercurrent is much deeper than the Cromwell Current.

It is also suspected that a countercurrent exists in the equatorial region of the Indian Ocean.

Caidin, Martin
  Hydrospace, E. P. Dutton and Company, 1964.
Engel, Leonard and Editors of LIFE
  The Sea, Life Nature Library, Time, Inc., 1961.
Yasso, Warren E.
  Oceanography, A Study of Inner Space, Holt, Rinehart and Winston, 1965.

25. Why does the sea foam?

Foam is made up of air bubbles separated from each other by a film of liquid. Bubbles coming together in fresh water coalesce, but bubbles coming together in salt water bounce off each other.

Most bubbles in the ocean are caused by wind waves, but they may also be produced by rain and even snow. The bubbles that form along the seashore are very small, mostly less than 1/2 millimeter in diameter.

When bubbles rise to the surface, they burst and release salt spray into the air, a fact well known to any wearer of glasses who has been on shipboard or at the seashore. Each bursting bubble causes a jet of several drops to rise to heights up to 1,000 times the bubble diameter. It is believed that most of the airborne salt nuclei come from bursting bubbles.

Blanchard, Duncan C.
From Raindrops to Volcanoes, Doubleday and Company, 1967.

26. How did seas, such as the Black, Red, and White, get their names?

Because the Black Sea is landlocked, it is deficient in oxygen, except near the surface. The high concentration of hydrogen sulphide causes a reducing environment, resulting in a black color.

Oddly enough, the recurring bloom of small blue-green algae *(Trichodesmium erythraeum)* imparts the red color to the Red Sea.

The White Sea received its name from the ice that covers it more than 200 days a year.

The color of the Yellow Sea is caused by the yellow mud which is carried by rivers, especially when floods occur.

Miller, Robert C.
  The Sea, Random House, 1966.
Stewart, Harris B., Jr.
  Deep Challenge, Van Nostrand, 1966.

27. What causes hurricanes and how do they differ from typhoons?

Hurricanes are great heat engines, much like the gasoline engine in a car. The moisture in the humid air over the sea is analogous to the gasoline in the gas tank; it contains the potential energy (or fuel) for the hurricane. Once the hurricane is born, it draws moist air up from the sea surface in a counterclockwise spiral to the condensation level. Here cooling of the air, due to reduced pressure, condenses water vapor in the air. This can be equated to the combustion cycle in the gasoline engine; it converts potential energy to kinetic energy.

The latent heat of condensation (597 calories per gram of water) heats the air, which then accelerates in its upward spiralling journey. It literally goes "up the chimney" formed by the relatively cooler air around it. At the top of the chimney of cooler air, the warm air spreads outward in a clockwise spiral (when viewed from above). As air spirals upward, through and out of the chimney, it draws more warm, moist air into it from below. This self-perpetuating process intensifies the circulation, causing the engine to run faster and causes the hurricane to increase in size.

The exact mechanism of hurricane formation is still unknown. Scientists know that very warm ocean water is required. The warmer the water, the greater will be the volume of moisture (potential energy) carried aloft. A storm must be some distance away from the Equator in order to start spinning, because the spin of an object on the earth varies directly with the sine of the latitude. There must be an outward (divergent) flow of air in the high atmosphere; otherwise the chimney would be closed off.

The origin of a hurricane is associated with an area where air converges and showers occur. This may be a remnant of low pressure from a cold front which moved far south; it may be an area of lower pressure moving westward in the Trade Wind Belt (easterly wave); or it may be an area where air from the two hemispheres converges (intertropical convergence zone). The origin could be due to oscillation of the great high pressure system which dominates the ocean.

Hurricanes and typhoons are alike in origin, structure, and features, their only difference being the area of the world in which they occur. Hurricanes occur in the waters adjacent to North America (North Atlantic Ocean, Gulf of Mexico, Caribbean Sea, and Southeastern North

27

Pacific Ocean); typhoons occur in the Western North Pacific Ocean. Because of the vast expanse of warm water in the Western Pacific, typhoons occur more often than hurricanes and are frequently larger and more intense.

Dunn, G. E., and B. I. Miller
   Atlantic Hurricanes, L.S.U. Press, New Orleans, Louisiana, 1960.
Tannehill, I. R.
   Hurricanes, Their Nature and History, Princeton University Press, Princeton, New Jersey, 1938.
Simpson, R. H.
   "Hurricanes," *Scientific American,* Vol. 190, pp. 32-37, June 1954.

28. How high is the highest wave?

An American tanker, the USS RAMAPO, reported the highest wave that has been measured with any degree of certainty. In 1933, while proceeding from Manila to San Diego, she reported a wave 112 feet high; it was produced by winds of 60-68 knots operating over a fetch of several thousand miles.

Most ocean waves are less than 12 feet high. Waves more than 25 feet high are rare, and waves in excess of 50 feet develop only during very severe storms.

It is very difficult to measure wave height from a ship. Height can often be estimated with reasonable accuracy by comparison with the freeboard of the ship, but accuracy decreases as wave height and ship motion increase.

USN Tanker *RAMAPO* – Feb. 7, 1933

Carson, R. L.
  The Sea Around Us, Oxford University Press, 1951; Mentor Books (Paperback), 1954.
Miller, Robert C.
  The Sea, Random House, 1966.
Stewart, Harris B., Jr.
  Deep Challenge, Van Nostrand, 1966.

29. How many species of fishes are there?

Although fishes are the most numerous of the recent vertebrates, there is little agreement among scientists on the number of species. Estimates range from 15,000 to 40,000 species; however, 25,000 appears to be the most often quoted figure. This discrepancy exists because fish species are sometimes named more than once due to inadequate descriptions and variation due to environment or geographical distribution. In some fish species, the male has been described as belonging to one species and the female to another because of a difference in body form or color pattern. This phenomenon is called sexual dimorphism. Other fishes have been named more than once because the young look different than the adults. In addition, most scientists agree that not all fishes have yet been named; the estimate of 25,000 allows for this unknown. The species of fishes with bony skeletons are more numerous than those with skeletons of cartilage (sharks and rays). Bony fish number around 20,000 while the cartilaginous fish number only about 600.

Herald, Earl S.
   Living Fishes of the World, Doubleday and Company, 1961.
Lagler, Karl F., John E. Bardach, and Robert R. Miller
   Ichthyology, John Wiley and Sons, 1962.
Norman, J. R.
   A History of Fishes, Hill and Wang, 1963.

30. Beside the whale, what other mammals live in the oceans?

There are several distinct groups of marine mammals, other than whales, that live in the ocean. These groups include porpoises, manatees or sea cows, seals, and sea otters. Porpoises belong to the same order (cetacea) as the whales.

The manatee is the fabled mermaid of old sailors' stories. Its forelimbs are absent, with the body ending in a broad, flattened tail. It lives in shallow coastal waters and eats aquatic plants only. Manatees inhabit the warm rivers of Florida and estuaries of the Indian and Pacific Oceans on both sides of the Equator.

The sea otter is very similar in appearance to the land otter, except that it is larger and better adapted for marine living. It has webbed hind feet, and its fur is said to be the world's best. At one time sea otters were very common, but they approached extinction because of the high demand and value of their skin. In 1911, an agreement known as the "Fur Seal Treaty" between the United States, Russia, Great Britain, and Japan protected fur seals and sea otters from further hunting or trapping. This treaty is still in effect and violation carries a very severe penalty.

The sea otter feeds on mussels and other shellfish and has a very interesting feeding behavior pattern. It floats on its back and pounds shellfish against a rock balanced on its chest; the pounding fractures the shell and enables the sea otter to feed on the soft parts. Sea otters are distributed along the California coast and among the Aleutian Islands.

Seals are divided into two groups: Those with external ears and those without. Eared seals comprise the sea lion, fur seal, and walrus.

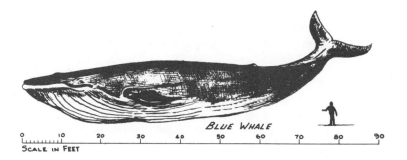

BLUE WHALE

SCALE IN FEET

31

The northern sea lion is the largest of the eared seals, weighing as much as 1,700 pounds. The California sea lion weighs about 600 pounds and may grow to be 8 feet long. The smaller female has a fine sense of balance, high intelligence, and is trained for circus work.

The fur seal is small, weighing only a few hundred pounds, and its fur is very valuable. It is found all over the world. Great herds spend the summer months in the Bering Sea and Pribilof Islands. The fur seal has been protected since the 1911 treaty. Only 3-year-old "bachelors" are taken each year for furs.

The walrus inhabits the Arctic and adjacent seas. It has a thick layer of skin and fat for protection from the cold water; it has two large upper canine teeth (tusks) about 3 feet long for digging shellfish and crustaceans from the bottom.

Earless seals comprise the harbor seal and the elephant seal. The harbor seal is smaller than the eared seals; it grows to 5 feet in length and weighs about 150 pounds. It feeds on fish and crustaceans. Usually harbor seals stay close to land, mainly around harbors and river mouths. They range from U. S. coasts to the Arctic Circle.

The elephant seal is the largest of all seals. The male is considerably larger than the female and may have a body length of 16 feet and a weight up to 5,000 pounds. The elephant seal was so named because of the large snout of the male. Distribution ranges from California to Alaska and they are numerous in the North Atlantic.

Daugherty, Anita E.
  Marine Mammals of California, State of California, The Resources Agency, Department of Fish and Game, 1965.
Scheffer, Victor B., and Dale W. Rice
  "A List of the Marine Mammals of the World," United States Department of the Interior, Fish and Wildlife Service, *Special Scientific Report-Fisheries No. 431.*
Scheffer, Victor B.
  Seals, Sea Lions, and Walruses, Stanford University Press, 1958.

31. What causes the tides?

Tides are caused by gravitational forces of the moon, the sun, and various other celestial bodies. The moon, being nearest, has the greatest effect. The sun, despite its greater mass, exerts only a secondary effect, less than half that of the moon.

High tides are generated on the sides of the earth nearest to and farthest from the moon. At times of new moon and full moon, the sun's attraction reinforces that of the moon, producing higher (spring) tides. Halfway between new and full moon, solar attraction does not coincide with lunar attraction and therefore the difference between high and low tides is less; these lesser tides are called neap tides.

When the moon is over the Equator as the earth rotates, a point on the earth passes through two high and two low areas each day. When the moon is north or south of the Equator, the two highs are unequal in height or there may be only one high tide.

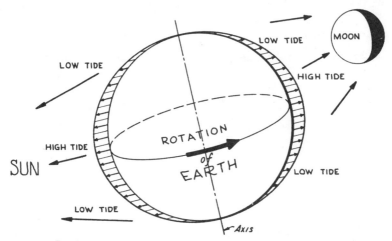

Engel, Leonard and Editors of LIFE
   The Sea, Life Nature Library, Time, Inc., 1961.
Gaskell, T. F.
   World Beneath the Oceans, American Museum of Natural History, 1964.
Stewart, Harris B., Jr.
   Deep Challenge, Van Nostrand, 1966.

32. Why do tide ranges in the same geographical areas of the world differ so greatly?

In addition to effects of the moon and sun, tide ranges are affected by shape and dimension of the coastline and sea floor. In some restricted water areas (bays, channels, etc.), heights may build up to 50 feet and tidal currents of as much as 10 knots occur.

Tides moving upstream in an estuary are slowed down by bottom friction, and the following water piles up. The water rises more rapidly than it falls, and the flood stream has higher velocity than the ebb.

Some areas of great tidal ranges are the Bay of Fundy, Bristol Channel, and the Sea of Okhotsk. The famous Bay of Fundy tidal bore moves more than 100 billion tons of water a day.

There are also areas in the world that are almost tideless; among these are the Mediterranean, Baltic, and Adriatic Seas, and the Gulf of Mexico.

Deacon, G. E. R. (Ed.)
  Seas, Maps, and Men, Doubleday and Company, 1962.
Gaskell, T. F.
  World Beneath the Oceans, American Museum of Natural History, 1964.
King, Cuchlaine A. M.
  Oceanography for Geographers, Edward Arnold Ltd. (London), 1962.

33. What are seamounts? How are they created?

Seamounts are relatively isolated features rising from the deep sea floor. To qualify as a seamount, a rise must be at least 1,000 meters above the surrounding topography. At least 1,400 seamounts have been discovered in the Pacific Ocean; this may be only a small percentage of the seamounts that will eventually be discovered.

The origin of seamounts is controversial. Their distribution in linear chains gives credence to the theory that they are caused by fissure eruptions. There is also speculation that seamounts were volcanoes that once extended above the ocean surface and later sank because of their weight.

Photographs of seamount surfaces show ripple marks which are apparently caused by deep currents; samples dredged from North Atlantic seamounts also indicate that they have never been near the ocean surface.

In the Pacific Ocean many flat-topped seamounts, known as guyots, have been found. A Princeton University geologist, Dr. Harry H. Hess, discovered guyots in the examination of echo sounder records while in command of a naval vessel during World War II. He explains the flat tops as wave erosion at sea level. If this is correct, there has been a great change either in the ocean floor or in the sea level, because the tops of the guyots are now 2,000 to 3,000 feet below the surface. Guyots are unknown in the Atlantic.

Ericson, David B., and Goesta Wollin
   The Deep and the Past, Alfred A. Knopf, 1964.
Gaskell, T. F.
   World Beneath the Oceans, American Museum of Natural History, 1964.
Stewart, Harris B., Jr.
   Deep Challenge, Van Nostrand, 1966.

34. How deep in the ocean can one see with natural sunlight?

Even when perfectly clear, water is at least a thousand times more opaque than air, because of the density difference. The depth to which one can see in the ocean is dependent on the amount of suspended matter and the angle of sunlight. Underwater visibility is best at noon when the sun is directly overhead; at that time about 98 percent of the light penetrates the sea surface. When the sun is at an angle of 10 degrees above the horizon, only 65 percent of the light penetrates; the rest is reflected.

Tropical waters usually have high transparency; the Mediterranean Sea, particularly the eastern section, is also noted for its good transparency characteristics.

As a diver descends into the ocean, the first change he notices is that everything appears to be blue-green; when he approaches the 100-foot level, it becomes impossible to distinguish colors. Light appears to come from all directions and there are no shadows. Cousteau reports that at 300 meters the pale blue lighting is hardly sufficient to define the shapes of objects a short distance away.

Sometimes horizontal visibility is better at greater depths because of the higher amounts of suspended materials in surface waters. Italian divers working on the liner EGYPT southwest of Brest, France, reported that visibility diminished as they went to a depth of 66 feet, then improved. Light faded as they reached the wreck at 396 feet; at that depth, visibility was 6 feet.

Caidin, Martin
  Hydrospace, E. P. Dutton and Company, 1964.
Cousteau, Capt. J. Y.
  The Silent World, Harper and Brothers, 1953.
Rebikoff, Dimitri
  Underwater Photography, American Photographic Book Publishing Company, 1965.

35. What is the volume of the world's oceans?

Estimates vary from 317 to 330 million cubic miles; the most reliable sources place the volume at approximately 328 million cubic miles. Ocean waters comprise about 85 percent of the total water on the earth's surface.

The volume of all land above sea level is only one-eighteenth of the

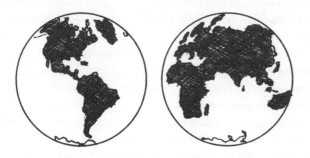

volume of the ocean. If the solid earth were perfectly smooth (level) and round, the ocean would cover it to a depth of 12,000 feet.

Bowditch, Nathaniel
   American Practical Navigator, U. S. Naval Oceanographic Office, 1958.
Engel, Leonard and Editors of LIFE
   The Sea, Life Nature Library, Time, Inc., 1961.

339-926 O - 69 - 4

36. Are whales found in all oceans of the world?

Yes, whales have been observed in all oceans of the world and even in fresh water. Most of the larger species continually migrate from ocean to ocean with the changing seasons.

There are two distinct species populations: the Southern Hemisphere group and the Northern Hemisphere group. Both groups breed in tropical coastal waters during the winters, then go to the Arctic or Antarctic regions for summer feeding. The Fin, Sei, and Humpback whales migrate seasonally in this fashion.

Sperm whales appear in tropical waters the year round, seldom going farther north than 40 degrees latitude.

Most people do not realize that dolphins are small whales; dolphins are also known as porpoises.

Two species, the Amazon dolphin and the Ganges dolphin, actually go into fresh waters of the Amazon and Ganges Rivers.

The distribution and migration of whales is studied by means of commercial catch records, tagging, and sightings.

Some whale species are in danger of extinction because man has overhunted. International agreements between whale hunting nations attempt to limit the kill of certain species of whales. Through this international effort, it is hoped that the whale stocks will be preserved for future generations.

Mackintosh, N. A.
  The Stocks of Whales, Fishing News Books Ltd., 1965.
Slijper, E. J.; W. L. Van Utrecht, and C. Naaktgeboren
  Remarks on the Distribution and Migration of Whales, Based on Observations from Netherlands Ships, Bijdragen Tot de Dierkunde, 1964.
Norris, Kenneth S.
  Whales, Dolphins, and Porpoises, University of California Press, Berkeley and Los Angeles, 1966.

37. Do any creatures in the sea other than the porpoise talk?

Yes, many creatures in the sea make sounds which may be a form of communication; porpoises and other mammals offer the greatest possibility for understanding by man someday. Dr. John C. Lilly, of the Communications Research Laboratory in the Virgin Islands, has reported strong evidence that porpoises (dolphins) can mimic the human voice.

Extensive recordings of whale sounds have been made. These sounds have been compared to the trumpeting of elephants. Killer whales in captivity have even talked to each other from one city to another over long distance telephone lines using hydrophones at each end as the receiver-transmitter.

Some fish, such as drumfish and groupers, produce drumlike thumps which are suspected to be a defense to frighten other approaching fish. Croakers received their name from the sound they produce, often described as sounding like rapid blows on a hollow log. Toadfish emit a "boat whistle" sound which may be related to reproductive behavior.

Among other noisy animals are sea lions, seals, puffers, crabs, snapping shrimp, and lobsters.

Herald, Earl S.
   Living Fishes of the World, Doubleday, 1961.
Lanyon, W. E., and W. N. Tavolga (Ed.)
   Animal Sounds and Communication, Publication No. 7, American Institute of Biological Sciences, 1960.
Marteka, Vincent
   Bionics, J. B. Lipincott Company, 1965.

38. How do oysters produce pearls?

Pearls are produced by a type of oyster more closely related to mussels than to the common edible oyster. These gems are formed by a foreign substance, such as a grain of sand, which accidentally enters the shell. The oyster attempts to reduce the irritation by depositing successive layers of nacreous material around the foreign body.

The most valuable pearls are obtained from oysters taken near Ceylon and in the Persian Gulf. It is believed that the nucleus of these pearls is a tapeworm egg.

Cultivated pearls are produced by inserting particles in pearl oysters. It takes 3 to 5 years for an oyster to produce a pearl; if sea conditions are not right during the entire period, the oyster may yield only a worthless lump of calcium. Under the best conditions, only 60 percent of cultivated oysters live to yield pearls and only 2 to 3 percent produce gem quality pearls.

There are many legends and stories about pearls. The ancient Greeks believed that pearls were created when lightning struck the sea.

Miller, Robert C.
   The Sea, Random House, 1966.
U. S. Naval Oceanographic Office
   Science and the Sea, Washington, D. C., 1967.

39. How far into the ocean can one "see" the effect of a river?

By using an echo sounder as eyes, one can "see" the effect of rivers in the submarine canyons that extend seaward for hundreds of miles from the mouths of some rivers.

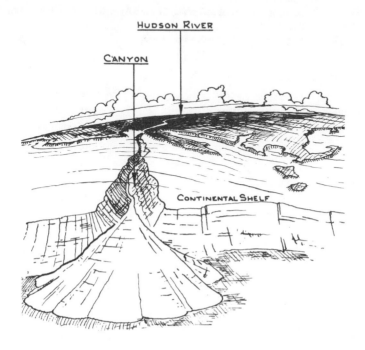

A submarine canyon 4 miles wide and 240 feet deep extends from the mouth of the Ganges River into the Bay of Bengal for a distance of more than 1,000 miles. The Congo Canyon has been traced for 145 miles to a depth of 7,500 feet.

Off the Hudson River a canyon extends 200 miles across the continental shelf. This canyon was surveyed by the Woods Hole Oceanographic Institution vessel ATLANTIS (cover illustration).

The continental shelf along the Pacific Coast of the United States is narrow and its submarine canyons are deep and steep-sided. The Monterey Canyon, off California, is sometimes compared with the Grand Canyon.

The origin of submarine canyons is still under dispute. There is speculation that channels may have been cut by rivers while the land

41

mass was above sea level, but it is probable that turbidity currents contributed substantially in creating these bottom features (see question 79).

Cowan, Robert C.
   Frontiers of the Sea, Doubleday and Company, 1960.
King, Cuchlaine A. M.
   Oceanography for Geographers, Edward Arnold Ltd. (London), 1962.
Stewart, Harris B., Jr.
   Deep Challenge, Van Nostrand, 1966.

40. Is seaweed a weed? What is it and how does it grow?

Plants as useful as seaweed can hardly be considered weeds because weeds are commonly defined as uncultivated (wild) plants that are useless, unsightly, and have no economic value. Seaweed is used as a food by millions of people, particularly along the Pacific Coast of Asia; it also serves as food for livestock.

Seaweed has many other uses, for example, as fertilizer, medicines, source of iodine, and ingredients used in preparation of bread, candy, canned meat, ice cream, jellies, and emulsions.

In the late 18th century seaweed was the primary source of soda until other sources became more economical and practical. In these years, thousands of tons of soda were derived from sea plants.

Attached seaweeds grow only along the narrow border near shore. Growth is depth limited because natural sunlight is needed for the photosynthesis processes of the plants.

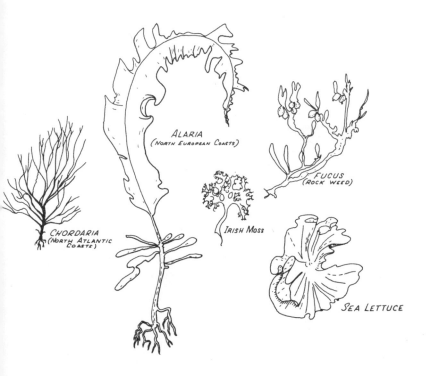

ALARIA
(NORTH EUROPEAN COASTS)

FUCUS
(ROCK WEED)

CHORDARIA
(NORTH ATLANTIC
COASTS)

IRISH MOSS

SEA LETTUCE

Floating seaweeds are found in great quantity in the Sargasso Sea, where sailors once thought it to be a hazard to ships.

Deacon, G. E. R. (Ed.)
  Seas, Maps, and Men, Doubleday and Company, 1962.
Miller, Robert C.
  The Sea, Random House, 1966.
Troebst, Cord-Christian
  Conquest of the Sea, Harper and Row, 1962.

41. What is green scum?

The green scum on ponds and slow-flowing rivers is formed by floating green and blue-green algae and a tiny flowering plant called duck weed. The duck weed and floating green algae do not live in sea water, but the blue-green algae do. These blue-green algae have a sticky covering and form slimy films on rocks and pilings. Mermaid's Hair, a large blue-green alga, forms thick feathery coverings on rocks and boat bottoms.

Algae are classified not by color but by structural relationship to other species of algae; it is "blue-green" algae that make the Red Sea red. Some "red" algae are either pink or white, and there is one "red" alga in the upper intertidal zone that is olive-green.

Dawson, E. Yale
   Marine Botany, Holt, Rinehart and Winston, Inc., 1966.
Miller, Robert C.
   The Sea, Random House, 1966.
Odum, Eugene P.
   Fundamentals of Ecology, W. B. Saunders Company, 1959.

42. What are algae?

Algae are primitive plants ranging in size from a single cell, which can only be seen with a microscope, to the giant kelps, which grow to a length of 100 feet. Algae are dominant in the sea, both in number of species (approximately 6,600) and in number of individual plants. Although algal cells contain chlorophyll and other pigments, these plants do not have roots, stems, or leaves. However, some larger forms do have structures which resemble these organs.

Algae do not need roots, because they live in a solution of nutrients and the whole plant can absorb water and nutrients from this solution. Some algae have a holdfast that resembles a root. The holdfast is simply a structure that holds the plant in place; it does not absorb water or nutrients from the "soil"; therefore, it cannot be called a root. Since most of the plant can absorb materials needed for sustenance and growth, there is no need for an elaborate system to transport water, nutrients, and food; therefore, algae do not have stems. The supporting structure of kelp that resembles a stem is called a stipe; it does not serve a transport function and it does carry on photosynthesis.

Some algae have blades that resemble leaves, but these are extensions of the plant body and are not the primary site of photosynthesis as in terrestrial plants. Because the entire body of the algal plant carries on photosynthesis, the blades are adapted to increase the surface area to make absorption and photosynthesis more efficient.

Photosynthesis requires light, and, since the amount of light available in the water is limited by suspended particles, the blades with their larger surface area enable the algae to receive more of the available light. When the water is very turbid, light penetration is poor and plants grow only in shoaler areas. Plants with large surface areas have a better chance of survival.

Large plants do not usually grow in the open ocean, but are restricted to water less than 300 feet deep; one exception is the sargassum weed which floats in the surface layers of the Sargasso Sea. Algae in the open ocean are generally one-celled forms and are limited to the lighted zone (surface to approximately 600 feet). These algae are extremely numerous and are referred to as the "grass of the sea" because they are the very beginning of the food chain in the sea.

Dawson, E. Yale
  Marine Botany, Holt, Rinehart and Winston, Inc., 1966.
Round, F. E.
  The Biology of the Algae, St. Martin's Press, 1965.
Smith, Gilbert M.
  Cryptogamic Botany, McGraw-Hill Book Company, 1955.
Zim, Herbert S., and Lester Ingle
  Seashores, Golden Press, 1955.

43. Can gold, silver, platinum, or diamonds be mined from the sea?

Diamonds and gold are now being dredged from the ocean floor in several areas of the world. Off the southwest coast of Africa more than one-half million carats of diamonds have been dredged from the sea floor since 1952. The ship ROCKEATER, owned by a United States company, is dredging about $200,000 worth of diamonds a month from depths as great as 200 feet. The diamonds are found in mixtures of sand, gravel, and boulders. Although the diamonds can be separated easily, the operation is not yet profitable because present dredging techniques cannot handle the large quantities of sand economically.

The coast of Alaska near Nome has attracted many companies interested in dredging for gold. Beach sands along the Nome Gold Coast yielded 100 million dollars worth of gold during the gold rush; these same sands are known to extend beneath the ocean. About 600 offshore prospecting permits have been issued, covering about a million and a half acres off the Alaskan coast.

Exploration is now being conducted along the coasts of North Carolina and Oregon to determine whether gold can be dredged economically in these areas.

Carlisle, Norman V.
   Riches of the Sea, Sterling Publishing Co., 1967.
Pell, Claiborne (Senator)
   Challenge of the Seven Seas, William Morrow and Company, 1966.
U. S. Naval Oceanographic Office
   Science and the Sea, Washington, D. C., 1967.

44. Where is the hottest ocean or portion of an ocean?

The hottest ocean area is in the Persian Gulf, where water temperatures at the surface exceed 90° F in the summer months. Near shore in shallow water, temperatures as high as 96.8° F have been reported.

A unique hot, salty area has recently been discovered in the Red Sea, where scientists of the Woods Hole Oceanographic Institution recorded a temperature of 132.8° F at a depth of 2,000 meters. In this area, the expected temperature at that depth is about 68° F. The reason for

these extreme temperatures is unknown, but much scientific research is being directed to continue observations in the area and to investigate theories on the origin of the heat source.

In the open ocean, maximum temperatures occur north of the Equator. The zone of maximum water temperature shifts with the season, but only in a few areas does it extend south of the Equator. Temperatures in the Southern Hemisphere are considerably lower than those in the Northern Hemisphere.

Dubach, Harold W.
   A Summary of Temperature-Salinity Characteristics in the Persian Gulf, Publication G-4, National Oceanographic Data Center, 1964.
King, Cuchlaine A. M.
   Oceanography for Geographers, Edward Arnold Ltd. (London), 1962.
Woods Hole Oceanographic Institution
   Research in the Sea, 1967.

45. How salty are the oceans? Which is the saltiest?

Salinity in the open ocean normally ranges from 3.3 to 3.7%. Oceanographers express salinity in parts per thousand; the symbol for parts per thousand is $\permil$. The average is about 35 $\permil$. The saltiest ocean is the Atlantic, with 37.5 $\permil$ in the northern subtropical region. The Pacific is less salty than the Atlantic because it is affected less by dry winds and resulting high evaporation rates. In the deeper waters of the Pacific, the salinity ranges from 34.6 $\permil$ to 34.7 $\permil$. The Arctic and Antarctic waters are the least salty.

Some areas in the world have abnormally high salinities; for example, the Red Sea and Persian Gulf have salinities exceeding 42 $\permil$. The "hot, salty hole" in the Red Sea has salinities exceeding 270 $\permil$ (close to saturation) at depths below 2,000 meters.

Very low salinities occur where large quantities of fresh water are supplied by rivers or melting ice. Salinity in the Baltic is 2 $\permil$-7 $\permil$ and in the Black Sea about 18 $\permil$.

Deacon, G. E. R. (Ed.)
   Seas, Maps, and Men, Doubleday and Company, 1962.
King, Cuchlaine A. M.
   Oceanography for Geographers, Edward Arnold Ltd. (London), 1962.
Dubach, Harold W.
   A Summary of Temperature-Salinity Characteristics in the Persian Gulf, Publication G-4, National Oceanographic Data Center, 1964.

46. Has a sea gull, albatross, or other sea bird ever flown across the ocean?

Some sea birds live along the coast and rarely travel far from shore. Others spend their lives over the ocean returning to land only to nest. Sea gulls are coastal birds, so they would not normally cross the ocean.

However, many oceanic birds banded in Europe have been recovered in North America. Kittiwakes banded by scientists in the Barents Sea area have been recovered in Newfoundland 4 months after banding. Puffins, fulmars, and petrels also are known to have crossed the Atlantic from Europe to North America, and the Arctic skua and the Atlantic cormorant fly from Northern Europe to the African coasts.

By far the most impressive travelers are the Arctic tern and the albatross. The Arctic tern, which is the size of a small sea gull, regularly migrates from its breeding grounds in the Arctic to the Antarctic. It molts in the Antarctic and returns to the Arctic to nest each year. The albatross is also an oceanic bird, returning to land only to nest. Banding records indicate that albatrosses fly around the world, especially during their first few years of life.

Belopolskii, L. O.
   Ecology of Sea Colony Birds of the Barents Sea, 1957. (Translation), Israel Program for Scientific Translations, 1961.
Salomonsen, Finn
   The Food Production in the Sea and the Annual Cycle of Faeroese Marine Birds, Oikos 6 (1): 92-100, 1955.
Solyanik, G. A.
   "Discovery of a Banded Polar *Sterna Paradisae* Brünn in the Antarctic," *Soviet Antarctic Expedition 2:28-31* (translation), 1959.
Vaucher, Charles
   Sea Birds, Dufour Editions, 1963.

47. Are there volcanoes under the sea like those on land?

Volcanoes have built up impressive mounds and ridges under the oceans. In many places these volcanic ridges extend above the sea surface as islands. Iceland is part of a ridge of volcanoes that also includes the Azores. The Hawaiian Islands are part of a volcanic chain that extends across the Pacific for nearly 2,000 miles.

On November 14, 1963, a new volcanic island began to rise from the North Atlantic, just south of Iceland. Fishermen witnessed the birth of the island, now known as Surtsey. Before the volcanic activity began,

the ocean at this spot was 425 feet deep. After the initial eruption, an outpouring of lava built up about an acre a day. One of the first scientists to arrive on the scene was Professor Paul Bauer of American University, who continuously observed and recorded the growth of Surtsey. His pictorial and scientific documentation of this evolutionary process as a day-by-day event is the first and only such record and should be a most useful record for research study by geologists for years to come. A 30-minute film is available on Surtsey.

Blanchard, Duncan C.
  From Raindrops to Volcanoes, Doubleday and Company, 1967.
Gaskell, T. F.
  World Beneath the Oceans, American Museum of Natural History, 1964.
Thorarinsson, Sigurdur
  "Surtsey—Island of Fire," *National Geographic,* Vol. 127, No. 5, May, 1965.

48. Is life found at all depths in the ocean?

This question was settled for all time in 1960 when Piccard and Walsh reported a flatfish, resembling a sole, at a depth of 35,800 feet. From the porthole of the bathyscaph TRIESTE they observed a fish about 1 foot long and 6 inches wide swimming away.

As recently as 1860, some scientists believed that marine life could not exist below 1,800 feet. This view was discredited when a telegraph cable brought up from a depth of 6,000 feet was found to be covered with a variety of marine life.

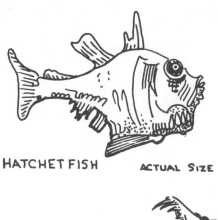

HATCHET FISH   ACTUAL SIZE

VIPER FISH
⅙ SIZE

In 1872 scientists aboard the HMS CHALLENGER found life in the deepest areas which they were able to trawl, but it was not until steam trawls and wire rope became available that trawl collections could be obtained from the deepest trenches.

339-926 O - 69 - 5

In 1951, the Danish oceanographic ship GALATHEA dredged various invertebrates from a depth of 33,433 feet in the Philippine Trench and a year later caught fish at a depth of 23,400 feet.

Deacon, G. E. R. (Ed.)
  Seas, Maps, and Men, Doubleday and Company, 1962.
Piccard, Jacques, and Robert S. Dietz
  Seven Miles Down, G. P. Putnam's Sons, 1961.
Soule, Gardner
  The Ocean Adventure, Appleton-Century, 1966.

49. What causes "tidal waves"?

"Tidal waves" are not caused by the tides, but by movement of the ocean floor. Their proper name is *tsunami,* a word of Japanese origin. They are also commonly called seismic sea waves.

Submarine earthquakes, landslides, or volcanic eruptions create tsunamis; a submarine disturbance may produce three or four waves with a wave length (crest to crest) greater than 3 miles, although their height over the open ocean may be only 1 foot. Speed of advance can exceed 500 miles an hour. As the waves approach shore, they are slowed and the water behind piles up to tremendously destructive heights.

Cowan, Robert C.
   Frontiers of the Sea, Doubleday and Company, 1960.
Gaskell, T. F.
   World Beneath the Oceans, American Museum of Natural History, 1964.
Stewart, Harris B., Jr.
   Deep Challenge, Van Nostrand, 1966.

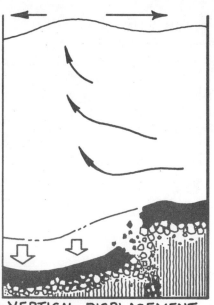

VERTICAL DISPLACEMENT
OF
SUBMARINE FLOOR

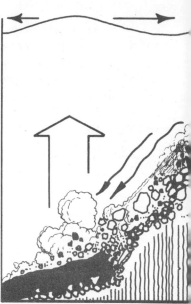

SUBMARINE
AVALANCHES

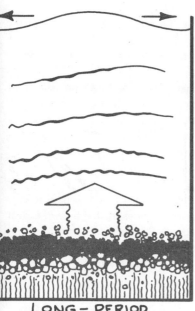

LONG — PERIOD EARTHQUAKE WAVES

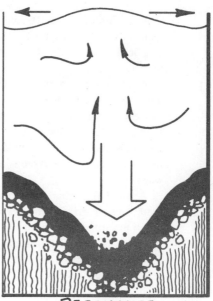

RESONANCE OF TRENCH WATER

50. Can "tidal" waves be forecast?

Yes, "tidal" waves (tsunamis) can be forecast, because the earthquake waves causing them cross the ocean in only a few minutes and can be picked up by seismograph stations hours before the sea wave arrives.

After the destructive tsunami that struck the Hawaiian Islands in 1946, killing 173 people and destroying 25 million dollars worth of property, a warning system was set up in the Pacific. Seismograph stations provide information on the time and location of the quake. If the epicenter of the quake is under the sea, a tsunami may result. When a quake is noted, tide stations are alerted to watch for indications of a wave.

A travel time chart centered on the Hawaiian Islands is used to estimate time of arrival of the waves. Warnings of estimated time of arrival are transmitted through an international Pacific-wide communication system. The U. S. Coast and Geodetic Survey operates the warning service, which has its headquarters in Honolulu, Hawaii.

Bowditch, Nathaniel
   American Practical Navigator, U. S. Naval Oceanographic Office, 1958.
Gaskell, T. F.
   World Beneath the Oceans, American Museum of Natural History, 1964.
U. S. Coast and Geodetic Survey
   Tsunami, The Story of the Seismic Sea-Wave Warning System, 1965.

51. What is the "bends" and how do divers become afflicted with it?

High pressure at depth causes some of the nitrogen in a diver's body tissue to dissolve in his blood. If he ascends too rapidly, bubbles will form in the blood and collect in his joints and bone marrow, causing the extremely painful condition known as the "bends." It is not ordinarily fatal unless bubbles collect in the spinal cord or brain, but the pain will continue for several days unless the diver is put under pressure and decompressed gradually; if the condition goes untreated there will be bone damage.

After a long dive, a diver is returned to normal pressure gradually so that nitrogen in the blood may be released through the lungs, avoiding the "bends."

Bond, George F.
"Medical Factors in Diving Safety," *Signal,* October, 1965.
Gaskell, T. F.
World Beneath the Oceans, American Museum of Natural History, 1964.
Rebikoff, Dimitri
Free Diving, E. P. Dutton and Company, 1956.

52. Are all fishes edible?

Not all fishes are edible. Some have organs that are always poisonous to man; others sometimes become toxic because of certain elements in their diet. In Japan, a national dish called fugu is highly prized. It is prepared from the puffer fish, and the gonads of the puffer are highly poisonous. For this reason, fugu is only served in restaurants licensed by the government.

Consumption of sharks and rays has been known to cause illness or death; this was probably because the victim ate a portion of the liver, which contains a very high concentration of vitamin A that the human body cannot tolerate.

There are 300 tropical species of fishes that cause fish poisoning; one type of poisoning is commonly known as ciguatera. A particular species may cause ciguatera when caught on one side of an island, but not if caught on the other side. These tropical fish are associated with reefs and do not usually venture far from the home reef; for this reason, the people living on one island may eat a certain species of fish, while those on a nearby island would not. No one knows what causes the fish to become poisonous, but most investigators agree that it is something in the diet. There is no method to determine before a fish is consumed whether or not it will cause ciguatera. Some common species of fish known to cause ciguatera are: surgeon fish, jacks, porgies, snappers, goatfish, moray eels, wrasses, and barracudas.

Scombrid fish, commonly known as tuna or mackerel, have been known to cause scombrid poisoning, usually because of inadequate preservation. The flesh of scombrid fish contains bacteria which, if the fish is not preserved soon after capture, begin to produce a histamine-like compound. This compound, if ingested by humans, causes a severe allergylike reaction and may even lead to death.

Fish, C. J. and M. C. Cobb.
Noxious Marine Animals of the Central and Western Pacific Ocean,
U. S. Dept. Interior, FWS, Res. Rept. 36, pp. 1-45.
Norman, J. R.
A History of Fishes, Hill and Wang, 1963.
Randall, John E.
"A Review of Ciguatera, Tropical Fish Poisoning with a Tentative Explanation of Its Cause," *Bull. Mar. Sci. Gulf and Caribbean* 8(3), pp. 236-267.

53. What other sea life is used for human consumption?

Fish are only one form of marine life used for food. Two other important sources are shellfish and algae. Shellfish are not fish at all; rather, they are members of two large groups of marine animals—crustaceans and mollusks. Lobsters, crabs, and shrimp are the most popular crustaceans on American tables. Spiny lobsters, Alaskan king crabs, and prawns are also harvested for food. Clams, oysters, and scallops are the most commonly eaten mollusks in this country. However, many other mollusks are used in some parts of this country and in other parts of the world. Mussels and cockles are popular in Europe, and squid is popular in Southern Europe and the Orient. Abalone is eaten in the Orient and the Western United States. One noted delicacy of the West Indies is conch salad; conchs are also used in chowder. Still more exotic delicacies are sea urchins and sea cucumbers; these animals are relatives of starfish.

Although not popular in this country, sea mammals provide food for many peoples. Whales provide a great deal of meat which is marketed commercially in Japan and the Scandinavian countries. The Eskimo has depended on seals and walruses for food, oil, fur, and leather for centuries.

Food from the sea is not limited to animal life. Seaweeds have also been used as food for centuries. In Iceland, *söl,* a red alga, is used as a vegetable during the long winters. Other algae have been boiled and made into puddings. Seaweed is also eaten in the British Isles. The use of seaweed for food is most highly developed in Japan. *Nori,* a red alga, is cultivated as a crop on nets or bushes set in quiet bays. In the past, Hawaiians have made use of a wide variety of seaweeds, and the most select varieties were grown in special ponds for the nobility.

Kelp, a brown alga, is the raw material for a gelatin used in many food products. The growing world population, coupled with the shortage of protein foods in underdeveloped areas, has stimulated interest in algae as a source of cheap protein. Flour enriched with protein extracts from algae has been used in baked goods.

Dawson, E. Yale
   Marine Botany, New York, Holt, Rinehart and Winston, 1966.
Hallsson, S. V.
   "The Uses of Seaweeds in Iceland." *Proceedings of the Fourth International Seaweed Symposium,* pp. 398-405, 1964.

339-926 O - 69 - 6

Hundley, J. M., R. B. Ing, and R. W. Krauss
    "Algae as Sources of Lysine and Threonine in Supplementing Wheat
    and Bread Diets," *Science* 124 (3221): 536-537, 1956.
Storer, Tracy I. and Robert L. Usinger
    General Zoology, McGraw-Hill Book Company, 1957.

54. What is fish protein and why is it important?

Fish protein is a substance containing all the amino acids essential to humans in proper proportions to maintain health. In concentrated form, fully dehydrated and defatted, it can be shipped and stored for long periods without refrigeration.

Protein deficiencies exist in areas of the world where starchy foods are used as a dietary staple. The critical areas of the world are the Far East, Near East, Africa, and Latin America. In these areas, nearly 60 percent of the people receive less than one-half ounce of animal protein daily. It has been stated many times that two-thirds of the world's population lack sufficient animal protein.

Roughly refined fish protein has been used as feed for chickens, pigs, and cattle, but it was not until February 1, 1967, that the U. S. Federal Food and Drug Administration approved the use of whole fish protein concentrate for human consumption.

The U. S. Congress has authorized a pilot plant in the Pacific Northwest, and plans have been made to set up demonstration plants in countries whose people have protein deficiencies. The purpose of the program is not to ship fish protein to other countries, but to help them develop their own industry.

Varieties of fish that are not presently used for food can be used for protein concentrate to supplement the diet of millions of people who are not receiving enough protein to maintain a healthy existence.

Food and Agriculture Organization (UNESCO)
The Director-General's Program of Work and Budget for 1966-67, C. 65/3, April 1965.
U. S. Department of the Interior, Bureau of Commercial Fisheries *Fish Protein Concentrate,* Reports 1-5, 1962.
Van Camp Sea Food Company
Potential Resources of the Ocean, Long Beach, California, 1965.

55. What is "fish farming" and where is it practiced?

For the most part, man's role is still that of a hunter rather than a farmer of the sea. In the future, however, it is probable that food shortages will require regulation of the life cycles of marine animals and plants in much the same way as on land. This might include altering the bottom environment, hatching of fish eggs, fencing breeding areas, fertilizing plants, and use of drugs to control diseases.

Japan has developed fish farming and aquaculture to a higher degree than any other country. Fish-farming centers have been established in the Inland Sea to offset the decrease in catch of high quality fish in coastal waters. Eggs are hatched and fries released into the waters of the Inland Sea.

By growing oysters on ropes hanging from rafts, the Japanese have increased the yield per acre to 50 times that of conventional methods. Oyster culture is also highly developed in the Mediterranean Sea where oysters are harvested from sticks thrust into the shoal bottom.

Off the coast of California old streetcars and automobiles have been dumped into the ocean to form artificial reefs to attract fish.

Possible methods of fencing sea areas include the use of nets, electrical impulses, and ultrasonics.

Fertilizers have been used experimentally in enclosed areas of the sea, but they have stimulated growth of weeds and unwanted species as well as of desirable fish.

Clarke, Arthur C.
   The Challenge of the Sea, Holt, Rinehart and Winston, 1960.
Deacon, G. E. R. (Ed.)
   Seas, Maps, and Men, Doubleday and Company, 1962.
Hull, Seabrook
   The Bountiful Sea, Prentice-Hall, 1964.

56. How far has a message in a bottle ever traveled on the ocean?

Each year, the Woods Hole Oceanographic Institution releases between 10,000 and 20,000 drift bottles off the East Coast of the United States to obtain information on currents in the ocean, particularly over the continental shelf. Clear 8-ounce carbonated-drink bottles are commonly used. Dry sand is added for ballast and a self-addressed postcard is included, requesting the finder to note the date and location of finding.

Bottles are released from ships, ferry boats, offshore towers, aircraft, and even blimps. The rate of return has been 10 to 11 percent. Records of all bottles released and recovered are kept in an IBM punchcard system.

Woods Hole has records of a number of bottles that have crossed the Atlantic from the United States to Ireland, England, and France—a distance of 3,000 miles. Other drift bottles have made a nearly complete circuit, passing the Azores and coming ashore in the West Indies after having drifted 5,000 or 6,000 miles.

Probably the longest undisputed drift on record was a bottle released June 20, 1962, at Perth, Australia, and recovered almost 5 years later near Miami, Florida. Oceanographers at the Tropical Atlantic Biological Laboratory estimated that the bottle had traveled some 16,000 statute miles at a speed of about 0.4 mile per hour. The most probable route was around the Cape of Good Hope, north along the Coast of Africa, across the Atlantic to northern Brazil, north along the South American Coast into the Gulf of Mexico, and through the Florida Straits to Miami.

Bumpus, D. F.
    "Bottled Oceanography," *Oceanus,* Vol. XI, No. 3, April, 1965.
Hubbard, Ralph
    "A Message in a Bottle," *Scholastic Teaching,* Vol. 14, No. 8,
    March 31, 1967.

57. What is the difference between hydrography and oceanography?

To explain the difference between hydrography and oceanography, the ocean can be compared to a bucket of water; then hydrography is the study of the bucket and oceanography is the study of the water.

Hydrographers are primarily concerned with the problems of navigation. They chart coast lines and bottom topography. A hydrographic survey usually includes measurement of magnetic declination and dip, tides, currents, and meteorological elements.

Oceanography is concerned with the application of all physical and natural sciences to the sea. It includes the disciplines of physics, chemistry, geography, geology, biology, and meteorology.

Physical oceanography is primarily concerned with energy transmission through ocean water, specifically with such items as wave formation and propagation, currents, tides, energy exchange between ocean and atmosphere, and penetration of light and sound.

Chemical oceanography is a study of the chemical properties of sea water, of the cause and effect of variation of these properties with time and from place to place, and of the means of measuring these properties.

Biological oceanography is the study of the interrelationship of marine life with its oceanic environment. The study includes the distribution, life cycles, and population fluctuations of marine organisms.

Geological oceanography deals with the floor and shore of the oceans and embraces such subjects as submarine topography, geological structure, erosion, and sedimentation.

The interrelationship of specialties is one of the main characteristics of oceanography. Oceanographic and hydrographic surveying may be combined on the same ship.

Many times the words "oceanography" and "hydrography" are used interchangeably.

Bowditch, Nathaniel
American Practical Navigator, U. S. Naval Oceanographic Office, 1958.

58. How old is the science of oceanography?

Mankind has been interested in the oceans since before the time of Aristotle, who wrote a treatise on marine biology in the fourth century B. C. The early studies of the ocean were concerned with problems of commerce; information about tides, currents, and distances between ports was needed.

While he was Postmaster General, Benjamin Franklin prepared temperature tables by means of which navigators could determine whether or not they were in the Gulf Stream. This resulted in faster mail service to Europe.

The beginning of modern oceanography is usually considered to be December 30, 1872, when *HMS CHALLENGER* made her first oceanographic station on a 3-year round-the-world cruise. This was the

H.M.S. CHALLENGER
1872~1876

first purely deep-sea oceanographic expedition ever attempted. Analysis of sea water samples collected on this expedition proved for the first time that the various constituents of salts in sea water are virtually in the same proportion everywhere (Dittmar's principle).

Even before the *CHALLENGER* expedition, Lt. Matthew Fontaine Maury of the U. S. Navy was analyzing log books of sailing vessels to determine the most favorable routes. He did much to stimulate international cooperation in oceanography and marine meteorology. The present U. S. Naval Oceanographic Office is an outgrowth of his efforts.

Daugherty, Charles M.
  Searchers of the Sea, Viking Press, 1961.
Guberlet, M. L.
  Explorers of the Sea; Famous Oceanographic Expeditions, Ronald Press, 1964.
Hull, Seabrook
  The Bountiful Sea, Prentice-Hall, 1964.

59. What universities and colleges have oceanographic courses?

Before World War II, only two universities in the United States granted degrees in oceanography. By 1966, at least 50 colleges and universities were granting degrees in oceanography, marine biology, and ocean engineering; at least 20 others offered courses.

Because oceanographic facilities and ships are expensive, most institutions offer a broad training program covering the basic sciences, mathematical sciences, and some introductory environmental courses. Normally, the oceanographic curriculum is available to those who have completed the bachelor's degree. Specialization in marine biology and marine geology is available to undergraduates at some schools. In June 1966, the Sea Grant College Act, first suggested by Dean Athelstan Spilhaus, now President of the Franklin Institute in Philadelphia, and introduced into Congress by Senator Claiborne Pell (Rhode Island), was passed. This project to develop and support universities in much the same fashion as land grant colleges is being administered by the National Science Foundation.

SCRIPPS INSTITUTION of OCEANOGRAPHY
La Jolla, California

A student interested in becoming an oceanographer should first major in one (or more) of the basic sciences—physics, biology, geology, chemistry, or meteorology. His later study of the ocean will relate to his past major. Most institutions offering degrees in oceanography require a bachelor's degree as a prerequisite. Oceanographers are expected to have mathematics through calculus.

Individuals planning to become oceanographers should begin preparation in high school; courses should include the sciences, mathematics, and a foreign language if possible. The best training for oceanography is to get into the "toughest" undergraduate science curriculum possible and to work hard.

Single copies of a list of colleges and universities offering degrees in oceanography may be obtained without cost from the National Oceanography Association, Suite 301, 1900 L Street, N. W., Washington, D. C. 20036.

Interagency Committee on Oceanography
  University Curricula in Oceanography, ICO Pamphlet No. 23, Washington, D. C., 1966.
National Oceanography Association
  Oceanography Curricula, Washington, D. C., 1967.
Oceanology International Yearbook, 1968, "Academic and Research Programs in Oceanology," Industrial Research Publications, Beverly Shores, Indiana, June 15, 1967.

60. Who hires oceanographers?

Between 2,500 and 3,000 scientists and technicians are employed in oceanography and related fields of marine science in the United States, and the number is growing. Most of these scientists are employed by colleges and universities and by university-operated oceanographic laboratories, where they are usually engaged primarily in research.

The Federal Government employs a substantial number of ocean-ographers. Many oceanographic positions are in activities of the Navy; the Naval Oceanographic Office in the Washington, D. C., area probably employs more than any other single activity. Government agencies with sizable oceanographic staffs are ESSA (Environmental Science Services Administration), with laboratories located in Miami and Seattle; BCF (Bureau of Commercial Fisheries) with laboratories at 14 coastal locations; and Public Health Service, with three shoreside research stations. The Bureau of Mines marine work is at Tiburon Island, California. Marine scientists employed by the U. S. Coast Guard and the CERC (Army Engineers) are usually based in Washington, D. C. A total of 22 Government agencies conduct oceanographic work of some kind. States bordering the ocean and Gulf of Mexico also employ quite a number of marine specialists.

Oceanographers are employed in limited but growing numbers by private industry (manufacturers and consulting firms), independent non-profit laboratories, fishery laboratories, and local Governments.

Board of U. S. Civil Service Examiners
   Your Future in Oceanography in Establishments of the U. S. Government, Announcement No. 371B, September 28, 1965.
Gaber, Norman H.
   Your Future in Oceanography, Richards Rosen Press, 1967.
Smithsonian Institution
   Opportunities in Oceanography, Publication No. 4537, 1964.

61. What is the largest oceanographic research ship?

The Japanese Arctic Research Ship *FUJI* is the largest ship built for oceanographic research, although larger ships have been converted from other uses. *FUJI*, which was launched in March 1965 has a displacement of 8,305 tons (full load). She was designed for breaking ice more than 20 feet thick, and her bow is heavily armored for driving the ship on top of the ice field and crushing it by sheer weight.

From 1957 until 1965 (when *FUJI* was launched) the Russian Oceanographic Research Ship *MIKHAIL LOMONOSOV* was the largest ship designed for oceanographic work. That ship has 16 scientific laboratories capable of performing any type of investigation or analysis. The scientific staff of 69 includes women scientists. Displacement is 5,960 tons.

The largest U. S. oceanographic ships are *DISCOVERER* and *OCEANOGRAPHER* with a length of 303 feet and displacement of 3,805 tons.

Capurro, Luis R. A., Albert M. Bargeski, and William H. Myers
Oceanographic Vessels of the World, IGY World Data Center A for
Oceanography and the National Oceanographic Data Center, 1961.

62. How are oceanographic observations taken beside from a ship?

Because oceanographic ships are expensive to operate, difficult to anchor in deep water, and limited in speed, continuous observations in one location and surface observations over wide ocean areas can best be accomplished by means other than ships.

Buoys have been used for many years to obtain measurements of surface and subsurface currents and temperatures, as well as to observe meteorological conditions. These observations were mostly made near shore because of the difficulties in deep-sea anchoring and long-distance radio transmission. More recently other measurements have been included, such as of salinity and waves.

There is increasing interest in setting up networks of moored buoys which would transmit oceanographic and meteorological information

by radio or satellite relay. The NOMAD (Navy Oceanographic Meteorological Automatic Device) buoys have withstood hurricanes and therefore supplied timely and useful data which could not have been collected by ships.

FLIP (Floating Instrument Package) is a hybrid ship-buoy. It is towed in the horizontal position to its location, where ballast tanks at one end are flooded, thus flipping it to the vertical position. FLIP serves as a stable, manned platform or "buoy" with observation ports extending to a depth of about 300 feet.

Offshore towers have also been used for collection of oceanographic data. Some, such as the Navy Electronics Laboratory tower located a mile off the San Diego, California, coast, have been built specifically for oceanographic research; others, such as the Air Force radar towers (Texas towers), were built for other purposes but also used as observation sites

by oceanographers. The Coast Guard is undertaking a significant and extensive oceanographic data collection program on its new offshore towers. These towers, which replace the lightships as outer channel markers to major East Coast and West Coast ports, are being equipped with an impressive array of oceanographic instruments.

Surface data, primarily temperature, have been collected by extremely sensitive sensors on aircraft and satellites. Frequent flights have made it possible to map the meanderings of the Gulf Stream.

Subsurface observations have been made by submersibles and by divers operating either from the surface or from underwater laboratories.

Cromie, William J.
Exploring the Secrets of the Sea, Prentice-Hall, 1962.
Yasso, Warren E.
Oceanography, A Study of Inner Space, Holt, Rinehart and Winston, 1965.

63. What is bioluminescence?

Bioluminescence is light produced by living organisms, both animals and plants. In contrast to incandescent light, high temperatures are not necessary; oxygen, however, appears to be essential to the light-producing process.

Thousands of species of marine animals produce bioluminescence; most of them are animals of the lower orders. In addition to single-celled animals, various jellyfish and related animals produce displays. Among vertebrates, luminescence is found only in certain fishes and sharks.

Displays are seen most commonly in warm surface waters. Although most of the organisms are small, there are such immense numbers present that brilliant displays occur when the waters are disturbed by the passage of a ship at night.

Luminescent bacteria are present in sea water, but not in fresh water, and can cause decaying fish to glow in the dark.

At ocean depths where light does not penetrate, there are strange-looking luminescent fishes. Beebe estimated that 96 percent of all the creatures brought up by nets were luminescent. There is controversy among biologists concerning the purpose of lights on marine animals. Some creatures have well-developed eyes but no light to enable them to see in the dark; others have brilliant light organs but are too blind to see. The property of luminescence is perhaps used as a defense against predators or as a means of hunting food or finding members of the opposite sex in the dark.

Cromie, William J.
  Exploring the Secrets of the Sea, Prentice-Hall, 1962.
Klein, H. Arthur
  Bioluminescence, J. B. Lippincott Company, 1965.
Yasso, Warren E.
  Oceanography, A Study of Inner Space, Holt, Rinehart and Winston, 1965.

339-926 O - 69 - 7

64. What is the continental shelf?

The edge of the continental shelf, where the bottom begins to slope steeply, most commonly is found at depths between 360 and 480 feet.

At the time the shelf received its name, it was thought to be essentially flat; now geologists know that the continental shelf has basins, ridges, and deep canyons. Compared to the deeper ocean floor, however, the relief is gentle; hills and basins on the shelf usually do not exceed 60 feet.

The continental shelf width varies from practically nothing to several hundred miles. The shelf along the east coast of the United States is many times wider than that along the west coast. If all the continental shelves of the world are included, the average width is approximately 40 miles.

The shelf slopes gently, at an average drop of 12 feet per mile, from the shore to the continental slope. In contrast, the grade of continental slopes is 100 to 500 feet per mile.

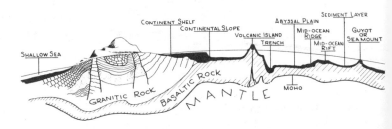

About 7 percent of the ocean is underlain by continental shelves. These are the areas where intensive mineral exploration is now being conducted.

Cromie, William J.
  Exploring the Secrets of the Sea, Prentice-Hall, 1962.
Engel, Leonard, and Editors of LIFE
  The Sea, Life Nature Library, Time, Inc., 1961.
Stewart, Harris B., Jr.
  Deep Challenge, Van Nostrand, 1966.

65. Has an efficient method of obtaining fresh water from sea water been invented?

Compared to the cost of purifying fresh water, desalinization is not yet an efficient method of obtaining water for either drinking or irrigation. Only in a few water-poor areas is it now economical to desalinate sea water. As commercially practical plants reduce water costs, the consumption of water will increase, making the desalinization operation not only attractive but also essential.

Use of water in the United States is increasing at the rate of 1.5 million gallons an hour! In many parts of the country water shortages are

already critical. Recognizing this crisis, the U. S. Congress in 1952 passed the Saline Water Act; this Act established the Office of Saline Water and assigned to it the primary mission of developing practical low cost commercial ways to increase the supply of potable water. Using the best commercial methods available in 1952, the cost of producing 1,000 gallons of fresh water from sea water was more than 4 dollars. Today the cost is about 1 dollar; future cost of 20 to 30 cents per 1,000 gallons is considered entirely possible.

A nuclear powered plant is scheduled to begin operation in southern California in 1972. Capacity will be 150 million gallons per day plus 1,800 megawatts of electricity. This one plant will produce more fresh water than all the desalination plants operating throughout the world in 1966.

There are a number of desalinization methods. Freezing of sea water leaves about one-third of the salts in pockets in the ice. Use of semipermeable membranes, ion exchange, and salt-eating bacteria has been considered experimentally. Scripps Institution of Oceanography is developing a multiple-effect sea water conversion system, which shows promise of producing fresh water for 20 cents per 1,000 gallons commercially.

The oldest method, solar distillation, is not economical, because even in the Sahara the cost of a plant would be four times that of an evaporation plant using artificial heat. Nevertheless, there are areas in the world where small quantities of water are needed, but energy sources and technical competence are not available. In these areas the simple solar still may be a partial answer.

Spiegler, K. S.
   Salt Water Purification, John Wiley and Sons, 1962.
Stewart, Harris B., Jr.
   Deep Challenge, Van Nostrand, 1966.
U. S. Department of the Interior
   Saline Water Conversion Report for 1965, Office of Saline Water, Washington, D. C., 1965.

66. Why is the Cape Hatteras area known as the graveyard of ships?

Cape Hatteras has earned its reputation as a dangerous area because of a combination of factors: sudden storms, shifting sand bars, and strong currents. The name "Graveyard of Ships" or "Graveyard of the Atlantic" was used by Alexander Hamilton, who as a young man sailed past the area. Later, he used his influence as Secretary of the Treasury to have a lighthouse built at Cape Hatteras.

The Cape is exposed to severe storm winds; it is open to the sea from north through east to southwest. Storms strike with sudden intensity. Hurricanes have driven many ships onto the beaches and shoals.

The sands of Hatteras Island extend seaward as gigantic shoals for a distance of 12 miles; at some places they reach almost to the surface. Sand bars on Diamond Shoals are constantly shifting.

It is in this area that the southernmost portion of the Labrador Current meets the Gulf Stream. At times, the current has great velocity at Diamond Shoals; at other times there is no current or its direction may be reversed. With northerly and northeasterly winds a dangerous cross sea is usually encountered.

Since the introduction of modern aids to navigation the reputation of Cape Hatteras has improved considerably, but the skeletons of many ships are reminders of its past.

Carney, Charles B.

"Hatteras: Climate Setting for Year-round Recreation," *Weather-wise,* Vol. 18, No. 3, 1965.

Lonsdale, Adrian L., and H. R. Kaplan

A Guide to Sunken Ships in American Waters, Compass Publications, 1964.

67. How does an oceanographic ship anchor to take observations in the deep ocean?

Although most oceanographic observations are made without anchoring, oceanographic ships sometimes anchor in deep water for several hours, days, or weeks to measure subsurface currents or to obtain repeated observations in one spot.

The weight of the anchor need not be great, because the weight of cable lying on the bottom may be more than 2 tons. The Navy often uses anchors of 500 or 800 pounds, but Danforth anchors of only 40 pounds have been used to anchor in water a mile deep.

In depths of 3,000 fathoms, wire tapering from 5/8 to 1/2 inch is normally used to lower the anchor. In greater depths, the taper is from 3/4 to 3/8 inch.

Free-fall anchors have been used for rapid anchoring in deep water. For example, in a recent mooring the total elapsed time for planting a 4,000-pound anchor at 17,250 feet was 16 minutes. No attempt was made to recover the cable and anchor. Even if a suitable winch had been available, the cost would have exceeded the value of the anchor and cable.

To prevent a ship from swinging on its mooring, it may be anchored fore and aft or it may tie to a bridle arrangement of three or four anchored buoys.

Pell, Claiborne (Senator)
Challenge of the Seven Seas, William Morrow and Company, 1966.
Sverdrup, H. U., Martin W. Johnson, and Richard H. Fleming
The Oceans, Their Physics, Chemistry, and General Biology, Prentice-Hall, 1946.
U. S. Naval Oceanographic Office
Instruction Manual for Oceanographic Observations, H. O. Pub. No. 607, 1955.

68. How much power (energy) is in a wave?

The kinetic energy in waves is tremendous. A 4-foot, 10-second wave striking a coast expends more than 35,000 horsepower per mile of coast.

The power of waves can best be visualized by viewing the damage they cause. On the coast of Scotland, a block of cemented stone weighing 1,350 tons was broken loose and moved by waves. Five years later the replacement pier, weighing 2,600 tons, was carried away. Engineers have measured the force of breakers along this coast of Scotland at 6,000 pounds per square foot.

Off the coast of Oregon, the roof of a lighthouse 91 feet above low water was damaged by a rock weighing 135 pounds.

An attempt has been made to harness the energy of waves along the Algerian coast. Waves are funneled through a V-shaped concrete structure into a reservoir. The water flowing out of the reservoir operates a turbine which generates power.

Bowditch, Nathaniel
   American Practical Navigator, U. S. Naval Oceanographic Office, 1958.
Deacon, G. E. R. (Ed.)
   Seas, Maps, and Men, Doubleday and Company, 1962.
Williams, Jerome
   Oceanography, An Introduction to the Marine Sciences, Little, Brown and Company, 1962.

69. Are the rise and fall of tides used to develop power?

Only in France are the tides used to develop power. There are many reasons why tidal power is not extensively used and probably won't be in the near future.

There are only a few places in the world where the tidal range is great enough to justify building dams. Even if all these areas were utilized, they could supply only one-tenth of one percent of the world's power requirements by the year 2000.

Labor costs for such huge construction projects are prohibitively high. Perhaps some of the dams could have been built 30 years ago, but labor costs today make the projects financially unattractive.

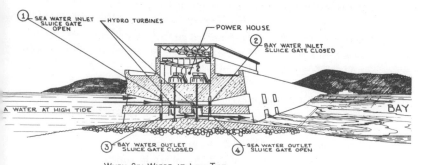

WHEN SEA WATER AT LOW TIDE.....
SLUICE GATES Nº 2 & 3 OPEN FOR BAY WATER
TO FLOW OUT TO THE SEA. GATES Nº 1 &4 CLOSED
WITHOUT STOPPAGE OF HYDRO-ELECTRIC GENERATORS
BY MEANS OF TIDAL GATE CONTROLS.

Tidal power cannot compete economically with power produced by nuclear fission and other methods. The main reason that tidal power is not used is simply that the need for additional power does not exist now.

It is interesting to note that extensive use of tidal energy for power stations would bring about a noticeable change in tidal conditions. According to the French engineers Allard and Gibrat, if the utilization of tidal energy is brought to 2 billion kilowatts, the earth would slow its rotation so much that it would lag 24 hours every 2,000 years.

Deacon, G. E. R.(Ed.)
  Seas, Maps, and Men, Doubleday and Company, 1962.
Gaskell, T. F.
  World Beneath the Oceans, American Museum of Natural History, 1964.
Pell, Claiborne (Senator)
  Challenge of the Seven Seas, William Morrow and Company, 1966.

70. Who is the most famous oceanographer?

This is a difficult question. The scientists best known for their exploits on and in the ocean have been explorers and aquanauts. Many men who have contributed most to oceanography are virtually unknown to the public.

One man who was both an explorer and oceanographer was Fridtjof Nansen, a Norwegian who froze his ship, the FRAM, into the Arctic ice off the coast of Siberia to prove the theory that an ocean current would drift a ship across the Arctic Basin. During the 3-year drift he came within 360 miles of the North Pole and then proceeded by sledge to a point 226 miles from the Pole. He is the inventor of the Nansen bottle, which has been the basic oceanographic instrument for decades and is still widely used. A special museum in Oslo houses the FRAM and many other Nansen mementos, awards, and expedition materials.

Lt. Matthew Fontaine Maury, USN, often called the father of American oceanography, was the first man to undertake systematic study of the ocean as a full-time occupation and to write an English language textbook on oceanography. The present U. S. Naval Oceanographic Office is an outgrowth of the work he started before the Civil War.

Two other Americans who contributed much to oceanography were William Beebe and Professor Henry Bigelow. Beebe, although best known for his work with the bathysphere in which he reached a depth of 3,028 feet in 1934, also directed a number of shipboard oceanographic surveys.

During his long association with the Woods Hole Oceanographic Institution, Bigelow contributed greatly to the coordination of physical, chemical, and geological studies of the oceans, leading to a more complete understanding of the interrelationships of life in the sea.

Many men who were famous for other reasons have been interested in study of the oceans. Included in the long list are Alexander the Great, Prince Albert of Monaco, Captain James Cook, Benjamin Franklin, and Commander Scott Carpenter.

Deacon, G. E. R. (Ed.)
  Seas, Maps, and Men, Doubleday and Company, 1962.
Daugherty, Charles M.
  Searchers of the Sea, Viking Press, 1961.
Lyman, John
  "History of Oceanography," *Ocean Sciences,* edited by Captain
  E. John Long, United States Naval Institute, 1964.

71. Does oceanography include the study of lakes and streams?

The study of inland waters (lakes and streams) and the processes occurring in them is known as limnology rather than oceanography, but many of the methods of oceanography can be used in this study. It is concerned with the interrelationships of chemistry, physics, and geology and their effects on organisms.

Processes such as sediment drift along shore are similar in lakes and oceans. Fish are affected by temperature changes in fresh water as well as in salt water. Pollution is a universal problem.

In North America, oceanographers and limnologists have a joint society, the American Society of Limnology and Oceanography, which publishes the journal *Limnology and Oceanography.*

Frey, David G.
   Limnology in North America, University of Wisconsin Press, 1963.
Pincus, Howard J.
   Secrets of the Sea, Oceanography for Young Scientists, American Education Publications, Inc., 1966.
Reid, George K.
   Ecology of Inland Waters and Estuaries, Reinhold, 1961.

72. What is plankton?

The word "plankton" is derived from a Greek word meaning wandering. Plankton includes all sea animals and plants too small or weak to do anything but drift with the currents. The plants are known as phytoplankton and the animals as zooplankton. Both are important food sources for fish and other animals.

The single-celled plants known as diatoms make up more than half the plankton in the ocean. A cubic foot of sea water may contain 20,000 plants and only 120 animals or eggs. Phytoplankton uses the nutrient salts and minerals in sea water as food. It, in turn, is food for many animals, which are themselves part of the "food chain."

Plankton "blooms" in the spring when nutrient-rich bottom water is brought to the surface by storms. Longer days provide more light to

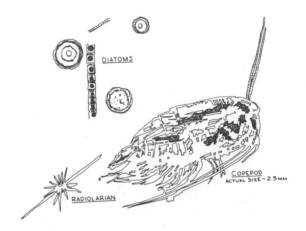

DIATOMS

COPEPOD
ACTUAL SIZE – 2.5 MM

RADIOLARIAN

stimulate plant growth and increase numbers rapidly. Phytoplankton may spread over miles of ocean, discoloring the water with shades of yellow, brown, or green.

Many planktonic organisms are sensitive to changes in temperature and salinity. Sudden changes can cause mass mortality, not only to the plankton, but also to the animals that feed on it.

Beside planktonic plants and animals, there is another group with some characteristics of each. This group includes the dinoflagellates which manufacture their own food, but also eat other organisms and have means of locomotion.

Deacon, G. E. R. (Ed.)

Seas, Maps, and Men, Doubleday and Company, 1962.

Engel, Leonard and Editors of LIFE.

The Sea, Life Nature Library, Time, Inc., 1961.

King, Cuchlaine A. M.

Oceanography for Geographers, Edward Arnold Ltd. (London), 1962.

73. Are there really sea monsters?

Although we discount the fabled sea monsters, such as the kraken which could swallow vessels whole, we have not yet explored the ocean thoroughly enough to say with absolute certainty that there are no monsters in the deep.

Scientific observations and records note that giant squids with tentacles 40 feet long live at 1,500 feet and that sizable objects have been detected by explosive echo sounding at greater depths.

Oarfish 40 to 50 feet long also have been observed by scientists. Either the oarfish or the giant squid with its long tentacles may have given rise to the sea serpent stories told by sailors of old.

In recent years, Danish scientists have studied large eel larvae that would grow to 90 feet if their growth rate is the same as eels of other species.

Helm, Thomas
 Monsters of the Deep, Dodd, Mead and Company, 1962.
Knowlton, William
 Sea Monsters, Alfred A. Knopf, 1959.
Miller, Robert C.
 The Sea, Random House, 1966.

74. What is sonar?

The word "sonar" was coined from the term describing the operation and functions of certain undersea equipment, "*sound navigation and ranging.*" Equipment using sound for underwater navigation and ranging is called sonar. It operates on the same principle as radar, but transmits sound waves instead of radio waves. Sonar may be either active or passive. In an active system, a sound is transmitted and the echo received. Distance is computed as one-half of elapsed time multiplied by speed of sound in sea water. A passive system is a listening system, and only direction can be determined.

The speed of sound is affected by water temperature, salinity, and pressure. An increase in any of these results in an increase in sound velocity.

Sonar is used for submarine detection, navigation, fish finding, and depth determination. The depth finding sonar is commonly called a fathometer but the correct general name for a depth finding sonar is echo sounder. The word "Fathometer" is a registered trademark of the Raytheon Company and should be used to describe electronic sounders made by Raytheon only.

Coombs, Charles
   Deep-Sea World, William Morrow and Company, 1966.
Hull, Seabrook
   The Bountiful Sea, Prentice-Hall, 1964.
U. S. Naval Oceanographic Office
   Oceanography and Underwater Sound for Naval Applications, Special Publication No. 84, October 1965.

75. How deep can submarines operate safely?

The maximum operating depth of submarines is a military secret; however, the engineering facts that determine safe operating depths are well known.

The bathyscaph *TRIESTE,* which reached the deepest depth of the oceans, is no more like a true submarine than a stratosphere balloon is like an airplane. A true submersible should be positively buoyant and carry a considerable payload. A submarine built by today's methods to withstand a depth of 4,000 feet would not have sufficient buoyancy to carry a useful payload.

Submersibles (not military submarines) have dived and operated under power at depths greater than 6,000 feet; *ALVIN* and *ALUMINAUT* are two of these. *ALUMINAUT* has a depth capability of 15,000 feet.

Newer construction materials, such as filament-wound, glass-reinforced plastic, produce high hull strength in respect to weight and may be used in the future for submersibles designed for deeper depths.

According to *Geo-Marine Technology* magazine (March 1967), World War I submarines had a capability of 100–200 feet; World War II submarines, 200–400 feet; and present day submarines, 750–1,500 feet. By 1970 the depth is expected to reach 4,000 feet; small, high-speed interceptor submarines may be capable of diving to 6,000 feet or more.

Hull, Seabrook
  The Bountiful Sea, Prentice-Hall, 1964.
Soule, Gardner
  The Ocean Adventure, Appleton-Century, 1966.

76. How do submarines navigate when submerged for weeks at a time?

When the nuclear submarine *NAUTILUS* made its famous voyage to the North Pole under the Arctic ice in 1958, the navigator was making use of Newton's second law of motion, F = MA (force equals mass times acceleration). The navigation system, known as inertial navigation, uses accelerometers to continuously sense changes in velocity with respect to a known starting point.

Three gyroscopes (one for each direction of movement) create a platform which remains stabilized regardless of maneuvers of the submarine. The system is entirely independent of magnetic influences; this is an essential requirement in polar navigation.

In addition to the inertial navigation system, submarines may rely on acoustic positioning sources on the bottom of the ocean to locate known points of reference, and they can make use of doppler sonar to determine accurate ground speed. The whole doppler-inertial navigation system on a nuclear submarine is tied together by an electronic computer.

Caidin, Martin
   Hydrospace, E. P. Dutton and Company, 1964.
Sherwood, David A.
   "Acoustic Navigation Systems,"*Undersea Technology,* Vol. 5, No. 6, June 1964.
Tilson, Seymour
   "The New Navigation," *International Science and Technology,* July 1963.

339-926 O - 69 - 8

77. How fast can a porpoise swim? Is it the fastest swimming "fish"?

Most porpoises can swim 17 to 23 miles per hour for short periods, although, to an observer aboard a ship, they may appear to be traveling much faster. There are records of porpoises being observed at 40 to 43 miles per hour, but they were swimming before a ship, utilizing the bow wave for extra speed.

Much research has been done to discover just how the porpoise is able to accomplish its high swimming speed. Either it is a much more powerful swimmer than expected, or it modifies its shape and, therefore, reduces hydrodynamic drag. The question is yet unsolved.

Although the porpoise is a very fast swimmer, it is not the fastest sea animal. Marlin, bonito, and albacore have been reported to swim at speeds of 40 to 50 miles per hour. The sailfish and swordfish have attained speeds of 60 miles per hour.

Alpers, Antony
   Dolphins: The Myth and the Mammal, Houghton Mifflin Company, 1961.
Lagler, Karl F., J. E. Bardach, and R. R. Miller
   Ichthyology, John Wiley and Sons, 1962.
Norris, Kenneth S.
   Whales, Dolphins, and Porpoises, University of California Press, Berkeley and Los Angeles, 1966.

78. What is the pressure at the deepest part of the ocean?

The pressure at the deepest part of the ocean is close to 7 tons per square inch, almost a thousand times the atmospheric pressure on the earth's surface.

At a depth of 3,000 feet, a pressure of 1,350 pounds per square inch is sufficient to squeeze a block of wood to half its volume so that it will sink.

At a depth of 25,000 feet, air will be compressed so much that it will be as dense as the surrounding water.

Bowditch, Nathaniel
  American Practical Navigator, U. S. Naval Oceanographic Office, 1958.
Carrington, Richard
  A Biography of the Sea, Basic Books, 1960.
Stewart, Harris B., Jr.
  Deep Challenge, Van Nostrand, 1966.

79. What are turbidity currents?

Turbidity currents occur when sediments on the continental slope are dislodged by earthquakes and begin sliding down the slope. A current is created by the increased density of the sediment-laden water. This current, in turn, dislodges more sediment which continues down-slope at greater speed.

Turbidity currents have broken off series of submarine cables; the time between the cable breaks enables one to compute their approximate speed. If the slope is steep and long, the speed may reach 50 miles per hour.

The sediment-laden currents cause scouring of the sea floor; it is believed that they contribute to the flushing and erosion of submarine canyons.

If the turbulence is sufficient to keep sediments in suspension, turbidity currents may flow for great distances; the sediments are finally deposited on the abyssal plains.

Cowan, Robert C.
  Frontiers of the Sea, Doubleday and Company, 1960.
Deacon, G. E. R.(Ed.)
  Seas, Maps, and Men, Doubleday and Company, 1962.
Gaskell, T. F.
  World Beneath the Oceans, American Museum of Natural History, 1964.

80. What is the most important discovery made about the oceans?

One of the most important discoveries about the oceans is the true nature of the sea floor. Not so long ago it was generally believed that much of the deep ocean floor was a featureless plain. We now know that there are numerous mountains under the sea, some of them higher than Mt. Everest. But perhaps the most striking discovery is that all oceans except the North Pacific are divided in the center by an almost continuous system of mountains.

Some of the other important discoveries are:

Discovery in 1938 of the coelacanth, a fish thought to have become extinct 50 to 70 million years ago, but which was found to be thriving off South Africa.

Discovery of a layer of living organisms spread over much of the oceans at a depth of several hundred fathoms (deep scattering layer).

Discovery of nodules of manganese, cobalt, iron, and nickel which can be dredged from the sea floor.

Discovery that the earth's crust is much thinner under the sea than under the land and that the bed of the ocean is underlain by basalt rather than by granite which makes up the continents.

Discovery of a deep sound channel that carries sounds for thousands of miles.

Discovery of life in the deepest parts of the oceans.

Perhaps the most important recent discovery is that man can live and work in the ocean for extended periods of time. Captain George F. Bond, a medical officer in the United States Navy, discovered that, once a diver's blood has become saturated with breathing gases at a given depth, decompression time is related only to the depth and not to the length of time the diver remains there. This led to the concept of underwater habitation by Cousteau and Link.

Carson, R. L.
　　The Sea Around Us, Oxford University Press, 1951: Mentor Books
　　(Paperback), 1954.
Engel, Leonard, and Editors of LIFE
　　The Sea, Life Nature Library, Time, Inc., 1961.

81. What is the MOHO?

MOHO is the name commonly used for the *Moho*rovicic discontinuity, the boundary between the earth's crust and mantle. It was named from the Yugoslav seismologist who discovered its existence.

The crust is the surface layer of rock, averaging 125,000 feet in thickness under the continents; under the oceans it is only 15,000 to 20,000 feet thick. This is why the planned Mohole was to be drilled through the ocean floor.

At the Mohorovicic discontinuity, the speed of earthquake waves changes abruptly, indicating a difference between rocks of the crust and of the mantle.

The objective of the Mohole Project (now discontinued) was to drill through the MOHO and obtain samples of the mantle rock. Some of the questions which led to the project are: How did the rocks of the oceanic crust become separated from the rocks of the continental crust? How was the crust differentiated? And from where did the layers of oceanic crust come?

Achievements that arose from the Mohole Project included development of ways to core the ocean bottom in deep water, a better understanding of the geophysics of several ocean areas, and improvement of drilling instruments and techniques.

Bascom, Willard
    A Hole in the Bottom of the Sea, Doubleday, 1961.
Ericson, David B. and Goesta Wollin
    The Deep and the Past, Alfred A. Knopf, 1964.
Yasso, Warren E.
    Oceanography, A Study of Inner Space, Holt, Rinehart and Winston, 1965.

82. How much do scientists really know about the oceans?

Every question answered about the oceans leads to additional questions that demand answers, so it can safely be said that our present knowledge is very small.

Charting of the ocean floor is one thing that can be expressed in percentage. Not more than five percent of the world's ocean floor has been charted with any degree of reliability and most of this was done during the International Geophysical Year (1957-58).

Our ability to predict the ocean environment is still small and largely restricted to predicting wave height and conditions for sound transmission.

Among the unanswered questions are the following:

Where can more fish for food be found? The Southern Hemisphere is largely unexploited.

Are there still unknown animals in the sea? The coelecanth (question 80) was unknown except as fossils until 1938.

Will "farming" the ocean increase our food supply without disturbing the balance of nature?

Were the Eastern and Western Hemispheres split apart millions of years ago as the contours of their present shorelines suggest?

What causes the lateral meanders in the path of the Gulf Stream?

How much pollution, radioactive and other, can the sea dissipate without turning into a "desert"?

Can a practical method of using plankton for food be found?

And, perhaps most important, can the nations of the world learn to use the ocean and its resources cooperatively? There have been many disputes over fishing rights; disputes over mineral rights on the continental shelves will follow unless international agreements are made and adhered to.

Coombs, Charles
  Deep-Sea World, William Morrow and Company, 1966.
Pell, Claiborne (Senator)
  Challenge of the Seven Seas, William Morrow and Company, 1966.
Woods Hole Oceanographic Institution
  Research in the Sea, 1967.

83. What are ice islands?

Ice islands are thick masses of ice which have broken from the ice shelves of Greenland, Ellesmere Island, or other northern islands. They have been used as drifting stations for oceanographic and meteorological studies. Ice floes of frozen sea water have also been used as scientific stations, but they usually last only a year or two.

The Russians have been manning ice stations in the Arctic since the mid-1930's; by 1958 they had airlifted 565 temporary scientific stations onto Arctic Ocean pack ice.

The U. S. station Fletcher's Ice Island (T-3) has been used as a research station since 1952. It drifts clockwise around the Arctic Ocean.

Another ice island, ARLIS II, was manned from May 1961 to May 1965.

Cromie, William J.
   Exploring the Secrets of the Sea, Prentice-Hall, 1962.
Thomas, Lowell, Jr.
   "Scientists Ride Ice Islands on Arctic Odysseys," *National Geographic,* Vol. 128, No. 5, Nov. 1965.
Weeks, Tim, and Ramona Maher
   Ice Island, The John Day Company, 1965.

84. What are the best materials to use for building a pier?

Because piers are constructed and used in all geographic climates and because of the variety of marine conditions that piers are exposed to, experts hesitate to recommend a universal "best material" for piers and other marine constructions.

Piers and harbor and shore constructions are subjected to corrosion, abrasion, marine borers, and fouling. Since World War II, extensive performance and service life tests of the basic heavy structural materials—timber, concrete, and steel—have been undertaken in hundreds of locations; on these basic materials an infinite number of paints, adhesive coatings, impregnations, and protective coverings have been tested. There is no structural material that can be guaranteed to withstand the extreme forces and pressures of waves generated by a hurricane or of sea ice driven by wind and current.

Results of experiments using steel piles for shore protection show the greatest deterioration at the beach surface. The corrosion created by the salt spray, combined with the constant "sanding" movement of the beach, causes this location on the pile to erode 10 times faster than any other.

In many cases, galvanic protection is given to steel piers. Galvanic corrosion occurs because sea water is a good electrolyte; the system acts on the same principle as a battery. Mill scale and other chemical and physical differences in steel cause it to act as a bimetallic, setting up an anode and a cathode in the electrolyte (sea water). Corrosion protection is afforded by attaching magnesium, aluminum, or zinc oxide bars below the level of mean low water; direct current using scrap steel or graphite anodes can be used to give the same protection.

Certain marine mollusks and crustaceans cause extensive damage to timber structures in sea water each year. The mollusks as larvae enter the timber through a small hole and grow to full size inside the wood; crustaceans destroy the surface, burrowing very close together and creating a system of interlacing holes that weaken the wood and permit waves and currents to break off the damaged wood and carry it away. Cases are recorded where untreated piles 16 inches in diameter have been severed in 6 months and creosote-treated piles needed replacement in 2 years! Such destruction has been reported in widely different geographic locations—Puerto Rico, Florida, Newfoundland, California, New York, and Alaska. Two common methods of pile protection are creosote pressure treatment and use of precast concrete jackets. The value of the latter covering is questionable, since marine borers are also known to attack low-grade concrete and soft stone. Certain tropical woods, such as Greenheart found in British Guiana, have a natural resistance to marine borers, but most woods must be protected.

Concrete structures tend to "grow" in sea water. A case on record cites a 13-foot-diameter concrete cylinder that increased 6 inches in diameter and 4 inches in height. In another case, a steel cylinder of 1/4-inch steel plate filled with concrete "grew", causing the plates to rupture. High-silica-cement piles covered or impregnated with asphalt have proven quite satisfactory; an engineering report on piers built with these specifications indicates that they were in excellent condition after 10 years of exposure and use.

Woods Hole Oceanographic Institution
Marine Fouling and Its Prevention, Annapolis, Maryland, U. S. Naval Institute, 1952.
Morgan, J. H.
Cathodic Protection, Its Theory and Practice in the Prevention Of Corrosion, Macmillan Company, 1960.

85. What is the hydrologic cycle?

The oceans are the vast reservoir from which moisture is drawn to furnish precipitation to the land. Even inland areas, such as the Missouri-Mississippi drainage area, receive up to 90 percent of their precipitation from water that has evaporated from the sea surface.

It has been estimated that about 9,000 cubic miles of water fall on the land surface of the earth each year. This water dissolves minerals from the earth and carries them, along with sediments, to the ocean.

Rain water may return to the ocean directly through streams or rivers or more slowly through subsurface percolation. Part of the water may be withdrawn from the cycle for extended periods by being locked up as ice, and some evaporates back to the atmosphere and falls again as rain or snow.

Thus, the essence of the cycle is the progressive transformation and movement of water through evaporation, precipitation, runoff, and return to the sea.

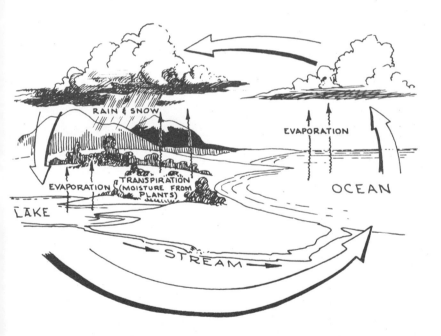

King, Cuchlain A. M.
  Oceanography for Geographers, Edward Arnold Ltd. (London), 1962.
Pincus, Howard J.
  Secrets of the Sea, Oceanography for Young Scientists, American Education Publications, Inc., 1966.

86. What is the DSL?

The deep scattering layer (DSL) is a widespread layer of living organisms that scatter or reflect sound pulses. During the day, this layer has been reported at depths of 700 to 2,400 feet, but most often between depths of 1,000 and 1,500 feet; at night, the layer moves to or near the surface.

Existence of the DSL has been reported from almost all deep ocean areas, except the Arctic, Antarctic, and some areas of the Central South Pacific. The types of organisms making up the deep scattering layer are still not definitely known. They may be fish, shrimplike crustaceans, or squid. Attempts to collect and photograph the organisms have been inconclusive.

The DSL produces a phantom bottom on echograms, which probably accounts for the charting of nonexistent shoals in the early days of echo sounders.

Dietz, Robert S.
    "The Sea's Deep Scattering Layer," *Scientific American,* Vol. 207,
    No. 2, Aug. 1962.
Soule, Gardner
    The Ocean Adventure, Appleton-Century, 1966.
U. S. Naval Oceanographic Office
    Science and the Sea, Washington, D. C., 1967.

87. How thick is the sediment at the bottom of the ocean?

Seismic refraction and reflection methods have enabled geophysicists to make reliable estimates of the average thickness of unconsolidated sediments on the ocean floor.

Sediments in the Atlantic are about 750 meters thick. The rate of deposition in the Pacific appears to be much slower (see question 4); the thickness of red clay sediment in deep basins of the Pacific has been found to be 100 to 200 meters. The average thickness of sediments in the Pacific is about 300 meters. Basins of the Indian Ocean have about the same sediment thickness as those of the Pacific.

Calcareous deposits in equatorial regions average 400 meters in thickness.

Most sediments (sand, mud, and clay) come from the land; therefore, the thickest deposits of sediments are near land. Thickness as great as 4,000 meters has been measured close to large land masses.

Cowan, Robert C.
  Frontiers of the Sea, Doubleday and Company, 1960.
Ericson, David B., and Goesta Wollin
  The Deep and the Past, Alfred A. Knopf, 1964.
Gaskell, T. F.
  World Beneath the Oceans, American Museum of Natural History, 1964.

88. What is a storm surge?

A storm surge is caused by a combination of meteorological and astronomical factors. Gravitational effects of the moon and sun produce tides. Storms, and particularly hurricanes, may raise the normal tide level by several feet. High winds blowing from one direction for a prolonged period (usually 10-12 hours or more) can physically "pile up" water on shore (or move it off shore). The effect is particularly noticeable, and most dramatic and hazardous, along shorelines of estuaries and semienclosed seas. This amounts to transport of a substantial volume of water by the frictional meshing of two fluids—air and water. When storms occur during times of highest tides, the results may be disastrous.

When the water level is raised, higher waves can result from the combination of greater depth and strong winds. The storm surge resulting from a hurricane can last through one or two tidal cycles.

In 1953, a storm surge occurring at a time of particularly high tides flooded the coast of Holland, killing more than 1,800 people. The same storm surge killed more than 300 people in England. Since that time, a flood warning service has been set up in Britain to forecast the probable height of a surge 12 hours before it strikes.

Deacon, G. E. R. (Ed.)
  Seas, Maps, and Men, Doubleday and Company, 1962.
Dunn, G. E., and B. I. Miller
  Atlantic Hurricanes, Louisiana State University Press, New Orleans, 1960.
Gaskell, T. F.
  World Beneath the Oceans, American Museum of Natural History, 1964.

89. What makes a very slight swell (wave) become much higher when it breaks on the shore as surf?

Until a wave approaches the shore, its height is usually about one-twentieth its length (distance from crest to crest); thus, if the crests are 20 feet apart, the wave height would be 1 foot.

When the water depth equals half the wave length, bottom friction begins to slow down the speed of advance. With a wave length of 20 feet, this would take place when the water depth is 10 feet.

As the wave slows, the back of the wave crowds the front, piling the water higher. The lower part of a wave, being nearest the bottom, is slowed more than the top; as a result, the top begins to curl over. When the wave height reaches three-fourths the water depth, the wave topples over as a breaker.

Bowditch, Nathaniel
   American Practical Navigator, U. S. Naval Oceanographic Office, 1958.
Deacon, G. E. R. (Ed.)
   Seas, Maps, and Men, Doubleday and Company, 1962.
Engel, Leonard and Editors of LIFE
   The Sea, Life Nature Library, Time, Inc., 1961.

90. What is "ship route forecasting"?

The shortest route between two points on the globe is a great-circle track; however, because of sea conditions, it is not always the fastest or safest. In one year (1954), more than 6 percent of the world's shipping experienced weather damage. Another 3 percent was involved in collisions, some of which were caused at least partly by weather conditions.

In the early 1950's, the U.S. Navy established a ship routing service which is a modern version of the service provided by Lt. Matthew Maury before the Civil War, when he gathered the logs of ships and produced charts of ocean currents and winds. Maury's work resulted in saving days or weeks in the journeys of sailing vessels; now time savings are measured in hours. By 1958, it was found that the travel time of Military Sea Transport Service ships from New York to Bremerhaven had been reduced from 10 days to 9.

The principles of ship routing are simple. Marine meteorologists predict wind speeds and direction for the area of interest. A chart is prepared to show lines of equal wind velocity and these are translated into charts of expected wave heights. By use of these charts maximum attainable speed can be computed for any type of ship. A ship using this service maintains communication with the individual supplying the routing service and receives a daily course to be steered.

Although ship route forecasting was developed by the military, private forecasters furnish the same service to commercial ships.

James, Richard W.
   Application of Wave Forecasts to Marine Navigation, Special Publication No. 1, U. S. Naval Oceanographic Office, July 1957.
Marcus, Sidney O., Jr.
   "The United States Navy Hydrographic Office Ship Routing Program," *Transactions of the New York Academy of Sciences,* Vol. 21, No. 4, February 1959.

91. How accurately can oceanographers predict ice formation, size, and movement?

The accuracy of ice forecasting depends on the locale, details required, time range of the prediction, and accuracy of the input weather information. Ice formation predictions are based on heat content and salinity of the water mass, currents, and expected heat exchange from water to atmosphere (weather prediction and climatology). The required heat, salinity, and current information is obtained by oceanographers aboard icebreaker survey ships when the ice coverage of the sea is at its annual minimum. From ocean data so obtained, the "ice potential" of the water can be determined.

With a known ice potential and expected air temperature data applied to the basic laws of thermodynamics one can derive the ice formation "forecast".

In the far north, long-range predictions of ice formation are accurate within 2 to 4 days. Farther south, however, where the environmental conditions tend to be more variable, the formation predictions are accurate within 8 to 12 days.

Size of the ice pack varies relatively little from year to year in the general area. Variations occur mostly on the southernmost fringes where shipping must travel; here variations are of critical importance. Predictions of the size of the pack are therefore generally quite accurate, but the predictions of ice in the shipping lanes need to be improved.

The movement of ice in and out of shipping lanes, or leads, depends substantially on the wind; therefore the accuracy of an ice forecast is dependent on a good wind forecast. An accurate 48-hour to 5-day ice forecast is possible because meteorologists can produce reasonably good wind forecasts. For long-range (seasonal) ice prediction, which must be based in part on the area climatology, the dates for opening or closing of leads on the Labrador coast may be in error by as much as 6 weeks.

Recently the problem of predicting "heavy ice" and "open" areas in the polar ice pack for submarine operations has been tackled by oceanographers using aerial and submarine surveys and wind climatology.

Oak, W. W. and H. V. Myers
"Ice Reporting on the Great Lakes," *Weatherwise,* Vol. 6, No. 1, Feb. 1953.
Perchal, R. J. and S. O. Marcus
"The U. S. Navy Hydrographic Office Ice Observing and Forecasting Program," *Mariners Weather Log,* Vol. 5, No. 6, Nov. 1961.
Wittmann, W. I.
"Polar Oceanography," *Ocean Sciences,* edited by Capt. E. John Long, U. S. Naval Institute, Annapolis, 1964.

339-926 O - 69 - 9

92. What is the International Ice Patrol?

The menace of icebergs to shipping was brought starkly to public attention on April 14, 1912, when the "unsinkable" ship *TITANIC* smashed into an iceberg off Newfoundland and sank with the loss of 1,500 lives. As a direct result of this tragedy, the International Ice Patrol was established; since that time not a single life has been lost through collision with icebergs in North Atlantic shipping lanes.

Seventeen nations contribute to the funding of the Patrol, which is conducted by aircraft and ships of the U. S. Coast Guard. Despite man's

knowledge of icebergs, his best defense against them is still to track their movements and broadcast warnings. Attempts to destroy icebergs by firebombs, gunfire, and chemicals have all met with failure.

Ice surveillance begins early in March when Coast Guard aircraft begin flying from Argentia, Newfoundland, and continues through June or July. The average number of icebergs drifting past Newfoundland each year is 400, although the number varies from less than a dozen to more than a thousand.

Icebergs that break off from glaciers of the Greenland icecap are first carried northward along west Greenland. They then turn westward and are carried southward by the Labrador current. The average time between breakoff and entry into the shipping lanes is 3 years.

In order to understand the forces of nature that influence the drift of icebergs, oceanographers of the Coast Guard make studies of the origin of icebergs, yearly crop and drift patterns, currents, waves, and meteorological factors. The Coast Guard is now using a computer aboard the oceanographic vessel *EVERGREEN* to aid in predicting the speed and course of icebergs drifting in the shipping lanes of the North Atlantic.

Bowditch, Nathaniel
  American Practical Navigator, U. S. Naval Oceanographic Office. 1958.
Kaplan, H. R.
  "The International Ice Patrol—A Memorial to the Titanic," *Mariners Weather Log,* Vol. II, No. 3, May 1967.

93. Who owns the water areas offshore and how far?

Ownership of offshore waters is one of the major problems to be resolved before the sea can be exploited peacefully. No country owns the floor of the open ocean. In the past, the traditional limit was 3 nautical miles, the effective distance a cannonball could be fired in the days of sailing vessels.

Now nations choose a distance between 3 and 12 miles from their shores. Within these limits they may exercise control of shipping; there is, however, no clear requirement for other nations to recognize this sovereignty.

Although waters were originally designated territorial for defense purposes, nations are now also concerned with protecting their fishing and mineral rights. The continental shelves are important for future harvest of marine life and minerals. The Geneva Convention of 1958 provides for a nation the sovereignty over its continental shelf to a depth of 200 meters or to the depth of exploitation of natural resources. Several Latin American countries have made claims of exclusive fishing rights to a distance of 200 miles from their coasts.

Burke, William T.
"Legal Aspects of Ocean Exploitation," *Transactions of the 2nd Annual MTS Conference,* Marine Technology Society, Washington, D. C., 1966.
Pell, Claiborne (Senator)
Challenge of the Seven Seas, William Morrow and Company, 1966.
U. S. Department of State
Sovereignty of the Sea, Geographic Bulletin No. 3, April 1965.

94. Is there any danger of overfishing?

In some areas of the world, overfishing is already a problem for some species. Stocks have been depleted in heavily fished areas such as the continental shelves of Europe, particularly the North Sea. Cessation of fishing during two World Wars proved that a decrease in fishing could result in an increase in the number of large specimens.

The U. S. Bureau of Commercial Fisheries has listed the following species as being seriously depleted: Pacific sardine, Atlantic salmon, Atlantic sturgeon, blue whale, fin whale, Atlantic shad, sperm whale, humpback whale, oyster, and sea otter. Depletion of these species is not caused entirely by overfishing; disease, predators, and water pollution all take their toll.

When the catch of a species reaches the point where the reproductive capacity is unable to compensate for the losses sustained, the species is headed for extinction. However, before this point is reached, operation of fisheries becomes uneconomical, and fishing of many species to extinction is thus prevented.

There is little agreement among fisheries experts on how much the world's fisheries could be increased. Estimates of the percentage of potential yield have varied from 1 percent to 75 percent. Undoubtedly the fish catch could be increased through exploitation of areas in the Southern Hemisphere and through fishing for species not now widely used for food.

Pell, Claiborne (Senator)
Challenge of the Seven Seas, William Morrow and Company, 1966.
U. S. Naval Oceanographic Office
Science and the Sea, Washington, D. C., 1967.
Van Camp Sea Food Company
Potential Resources of the Ocean, Long Beach, California, 1965.

95. Are radioactive wastes disposed in the ocean? If so, where and how, and are there any latent dangers involved?

Radioactive wastes in concentrations considered harmful to man are contained in storage tanks on land; only low-level concentrations are disposed in the ocean in sealed containers.

Nuclear generators of electricity will produce large quantities of low-level radioactive wastes. The sea has a great capacity for dispersing contaminants; however, certain marine organisms have the capacity to concentrate radioactive and other materials, even in an environment with low levels of concentration. Clams and other sessile (permanently attached) organisms eaten by man concentrate strontium-90 in their bodies; fish also concentrate the material in their bodies. Local game and fish authorities should be consulted before consumption of organisms taken from waters containing even low-level radioactive contaminants.

Some Russian scientists are of the opinion that disposal of radioactive waste in the sea is potentially harmful, especially if it reaches the sea at times when fish eggs are developing.

While this view is not shared by all scientists, it does nevertheless suggest a latent danger: any disposal of radioactive materials in the sea is potentially hazardous. The study of organism uptake and concentration of elements in sea water to such an extent that they may become inedible is a subject that promises to receive increasing attention and study by health and Government scientists and authorities.

Cowan, Robert C.
   Frontiers of the Sea, Doubleday and Company, 1960.
Stewart, Harris B., Jr.
   Deep Challenge, Van Nostrand, 1966.
Williams, Jerome
   Oceanography, An Introduction to the Marine Sciences, Little, Brown and Company, 1962.

96. Why isn't there more interest and activity in recovery of sunken ships and treasure?

There is a great deal of interest in sunken ships and treasures, not only among professional salvors, but also among historical researchers and adventurers, including the armchair variety. From the beginning of time, men have been fascinated by the thought of getting rich quickly; but, for every successful treasure hunter, there are hundreds who don't even meet expenses.

Unquestionably, gold worth millions of dollars lies on the bottom of the ocean. It has been estimated that 150 million dollars worth of treasure from Spanish ships which sank while crossing from the Caribbean to Spain has never been salvaged.

The availability of scuba gear has opened the search beneath the sea to amateurs. Those who search in shallow water (less than 65 feet) are almost certain to be disappointed; most treasure ships in these depths were located and salvaged soon after their loss.

Waters between 65 feet and 200 feet deep (the effective working depth of scuba gear) offer most hope of finding treasure without expenditure of large capital. The hazards of salvage operations in deep water are great, and professional salvors must have a substantive margin of potential profits, because bad weather and equipment breakdown can make the operation expensive. Old wrecks are nearly always covered by coral, sand, and mud. Poor visibility adds to the difficulty of salvage operations. Traditionally, there is an old shark guarding every treasure.

115

There are fabulous true stories, such as the success of Wagner and Associates, who have recovered more than a million dollars in treasure from Spanish ships off the coast of Florida. Perhaps there would be more such stories if it were not for the fact that successful treasure hunters are often closemouthed.

Not all the treasures on the ocean bottom are gold and silver. When the ANDREA DORIA sank in 240 feet of water in 1956, she carried with her irreplaceable paintings of Rembrandt, which may still be undamaged by salt water. A life-size bronze statue of Admiral Doria has already been salvaged.

Two ships which sailed the seas many years ago will become national treasures of their respective countries when salvage and renovation are completed. The VASA, which sank in Stockholm (Sweden) harbor on her maiden voyage in 1628, was raised in 1961 and is now being restored. Eventually, the VASA and the artifacts found aboard will reside in their own seaside museum. In the United States, work is actively proceeding to raise from Mobile Bay (Alabama) the Yankee Civil War ironsided monitor known officially as USS TECUMSEH. Some objects have already been recovered from the ship, but many more museum pieces are expected to be located when the ship surfaces. When restored, the USS TECUMSEH will become a prize historic relic in the Smithsonian collection. Both ship and artifacts are valued beyond any price.

Lonsdale, Adrian L., and H. R. Kaplan
   A Guide to Sunken Ships in American Waters, Compass Publications, 1964.
Potter, John S., Jr.
   The Treasure Diver's Guide, Doubleday and Company, 1960.
Wagner, Kip
   "Drowned Galleons Yield Spanish Gold," *National Geographic,* Vol. 127, No. 1, January 1965.

97. What types of organisms, other than sharks, are potentially dangerous to swimmers?

The most dangerous animal other than sharks is probably the barracuda; indeed it is feared more than sharks by West Indian divers. Its usual length is only 4 to 6 feet, but it is aggressive, fast, and armed with a combination of long canines and small teeth capable of cutting as cleanly as a knife.

Although no authentic record of deliberate attacks on man exists, the killer whale is potentially more dangerous than either sharks or barracudas. This carnivore measures 15 to 20 feet and hunts in packs. It attacks, seals, walruses, porpoises, and even baleen whales.

The moray eel, which is as long as 10 feet, lurks in holes in coral reefs and may inflict severe lacerations on a diver who pokes his hand into its hiding place, or it may grasp the diver in its bulldoglike grip until he drowns.

The octopus is probably overrated as a villain because of its evil appearance; nevertheless, its bite is poisonous. The giant squid has been known to pull man beneath the water to his death. The Portuguese man-of-war has tentacles up to 50 feet long with stinging cells which are painful to a swimmer brushing against them.

There is a large group of animals dangerous to swimmers or waders who step on them. These include the sting ray, stonefish, zebra fish, toadfish, and many others. The giant tropical clam *(Tridacna),* weighing as much as 500 pounds, has been depicted as trapping divers; however, no authentic records exist.

Cromie, William J.
   The Living World of the Sea, Prentice-Hall, 1966.
Engel, Leonard and Editors of LIFE
   The Sea, Life Nature Library, Time, Inc., 1961.
Herald, Earl S.
   Living Fishes of the World, Doubleday, 1961.

98. How much electricity does an electric eel generate?

Although the electric eel (which isn't a true eel) is the best known generator of electricity, there are at least 500 kinds of fishes that generate appreciable amounts of electricity. The electrical discharge serves to stun prey and repel attackers.

The average discharge is more than 350 volts, but discharges as high as 650 volts have been measured. Current is low, usually a fraction of an ampere; however, brief discharges of 500 volts at 2 amperes have been measured, producing 1,000 watts. Although direct current is produced, it may be discharged as frequently as 300 times a second.

Severity of the shock depends on the size and state of health of the fish. Voltage increases until the eel reaches a total length of about 3 feet; after that, only amperage increases. Electric eels in South American waters have been known to grow to a length of almost 10 feet.

Other electric fish are found in other parts of the world.

Cromie, William J.
    The Living World of the Sea, Prentice-Hall, 1966.
Herald, Earl S.
    Living Fishes of the World, Doubleday and Company, 1961.

99. How are ships protected from corrosion and fouling?

In the days of wooden ships, copper sheathing was used for protection against fouling organisms because of its toxic properties. It served the additional purpose of protecting the hull against borers. By 1783 all English vessels were copper sheathed, and by the early 1800's the French and Spanish had followed suit. Copper sheathing has now been replaced by coatings and paints, many of which contain copper. Because the toxic material must dissolve fast enough to prevent attachment, these coatings must be renewed periodically.

Before World War II, development of antifouling coatings was on a trial-and-error basis. During the war, oceanographers of the Woods Hole Oceanographic Institution worked with the U. S. Navy to learn how marine paint actually works and which compounds are most effective at the least cost. Their research saved millions of dollars by cutting the cost of paints, lengthening the stay out of dry dock, and saving fuel. The Navy attributed a 10-percent fuel bill reduction to the improved antifouling paints.

Corrosion of ships' hulls is prevented by organic coatings or cathodic protection. Sea water is very corrosive, and the copper and mercury compounds used in antifouling paints, if not isolated from the hull, may accelerate corrosion. The most widely used anticorrosive compounds are vinyls, epoxies, and combinations of epoxy and coal tar. Fiberglass coatings are being tested.

When a metal corrodes, metal ions enter the electrolyte (sea water) at the anode, leaving behind electrons which flow to the cathode through the metal. In cathodic protection, the corrosion potential of the hull is made more electronegative and the direction of flow is reversed at the sacrifice of the cathodic metal.

Nowacki, Louis J., and Walter K. Boyd
   Metals Protection in the Marine Environment, Battelle Technical Review, June 1964.
Turner, Harry J., Jr.
   "A Practical Approach to Marine Fouling," *Geo-Marine Technology,* Vol. 3, No. 3, March 1967.

100. What causes the hydrogen sulphide concentration at the bottom of the Black Sea?

The Black Sea is landlocked with only a narrow, shallow outlet to the Mediterranean Sea. As a result of its configuration, the bottom water is stagnant. Although the surface water is well oxygenated and teeming with life, water below the depth of about 200 meters contains no oxygen and is inhabited only by bacteria that decompose organic matter drifting down from above.

Decomposition of organic material on the bottom uses up any available oxygen so that hydrogen sulphide is concentrated in a thick layer of bottom water. This hydrogen sulphide colors the black mud on the sea floor.

Similar conditions occur in those Norwegian fiords that are separated from the open ocean by shallow sills.

Miller, Robert C.
   The Sea, Random House, 1966.
Sverdrup, H. V., Martin W. Johnson, and Richard H. Fleming
   The Oceans, Their Physics, Chemistry and General Biology, Prentice-Hall, 1946.

They that go down to the sea in ships,

That do business in great waters,

These see the works of the LORD,

And His wonders in the deep.

— Psalms 107:23-24

U. S. GOVERNMENT PRINTING OFFICE : 1969 O - 339-926